幻境　海洋微化石　微美

MICROFOSSIL

THE EXQUISITE BEAUTY UNDER THE SEA

館長 序

　　國立臺灣博物館成立於 1908 年，是臺灣現存歷史最悠久的博物館，目前累積藏品已逾 11 萬件，在地球科學、人類學、植物學及動物學等四大學門領域的研究、典藏、展示與教育推廣，一向不遺餘力，百年來見證臺灣自然與人文的演變，是民眾深入認識臺灣的櫥窗。

　　化石是地球科學學門重要的類別之一。國立臺灣博物館土銀展示館展出的特暴龍、迅掠龍、三角龍及翼龍等恐龍化石標本，長期以來廣受青少年喜愛。土銀展示館展出古老地質時期的化石，如古生代的三葉蟲、中生代的恐龍、新生代的長毛象等化石，是認識地球生命起源及史前生物的最佳學習場域。相較於前述體型巨大的化石展示，本館特別與臺北市立大學合辦「微美幻境特展」，在經濟部中央地質調查所、台灣中油股份有限公司、國立自然科學博物館、國立中山大學海洋科學系、國立中正大學地球與環境科學系、樹谷生活科學館等協辦單位的齊力協助下，將歷年東西方科學界前輩與各單位重要的研究成果，透過展覽來呈現人類眼睛無法辨識的微化石之美及其重要的科學意義。

　　本館為配合「微美幻境特展」發行專書，內容主要由微化石的種類談起，帶領民眾認識有孔蟲、放射蟲、矽藻和鈣板藻等四種化石；欣賞這些人類眼睛難以辨識的微化石個體，經過構思可得到如美術館級作品般的藝術創作；藉由微化石科學史的珍貴線裝古籍及各國郵票展示，瞭解微化石如何成為油田探勘、環境變遷研究的重要線索，讓人深刻感受到造化之神奇。

國立臺灣博物館

洪世佑 館長

策展人 序

　　我們居住的藍色星球約有百分之七十的面積為海水所覆蓋,海洋中數量眾多、體型極微的各式浮游生物,不單是海中食物鏈金字塔的基礎,更是影響海洋生物多樣性的關鍵。這些單細胞的微體生物出現在地球的時間極其久遠,少數類別擁有能保存為化石的殼體或骨架,死後成為海床沉積物的組成物質,通稱為微化石。

　　以人類眼睛難以辨識的這些微化石個體,經不同倍率的顯微技術放大後,其變化多端的殼體與骨架,每一個體都充滿獨特、幾何、結構之美,令人深刻感受自然造化之神奇。這些微化石雖因個體小而常被人們忽視,但您可能不知道這些微體生物的平凡功能,竟然還包括對於地球氣候扮演調控角色呢。

　　臺博館與臺北市立大學合作挑選微化石最具型態之美的有孔蟲、鈣板藻、矽藻與放射蟲為主題辦理「微美幻境特展」,希望藉由科技與藝術的結合,探尋微化石在近代科學發展歷程的軌跡。從早期顯微觀察的精美版畫,到西方學者開創微體古生物學的啟蒙階段,直到臺灣地質調查工作的多元面貌。

　　本書即配合「微美幻境特展」出版,內容著重於前述微生物化石之美外,亦期待傳承微化石的地科知識。

臺北市立大學
地球環境暨生物資源學系

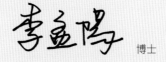 博士

國立臺灣博物館
典藏管理組

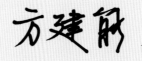 博士

目錄
Contents

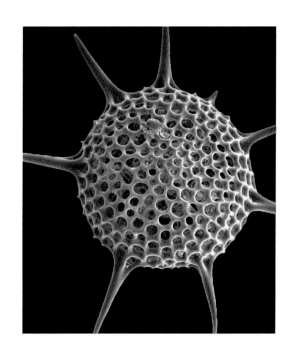

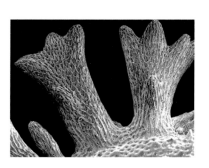

1

微化石美術館
Museum of Microfossil

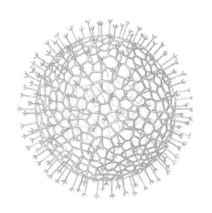

> 我們已經來到陌生世界的邊緣，在這裡，一切成見都必須拋棄。
>
> *We have come to the edge of a world of which we have no experience, and where all our preconceptions must be recast.*

—— 達西·湯普生（*D'Arcy Thompson, 1860 - 1948*）

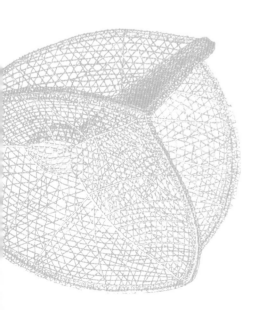

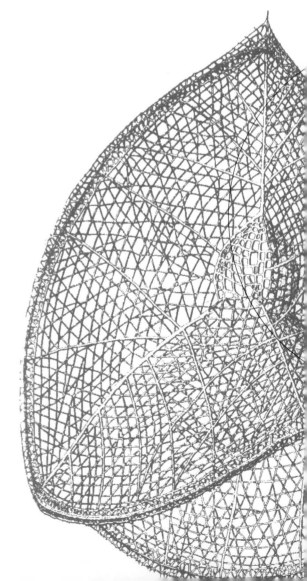

8

浮游國度
The Plankton World

浮游國度 The Plankton World

浩瀚大洋深處的沉積物之中，藏有許多個體大小如塵埃的微化
石。這些肉眼難以辨識的微小生命，許多曾度過短暫一生於陽光
燦爛的浮游國度，死亡後飄落至幽冥深海而長眠於此，也有世代
定居於此者。

在不同倍率的顯微放大後，微化石蘊藏變化多端的殼體與骨架，
最具形態之美的包括有孔蟲、放射蟲、矽藻與鈣板藻，每一個體
都充滿原創、幾何、結構之美，令人深刻感受造化之神奇。

Hidden in the deep ocean sediments are microfossils with size
as little as dust. Many of these hardly discernible creatures once
lived floating in the sunlit shallow waters, and settled down to the
seabed after the end of their life, joining those benthos lived at the
bottom of the ocean for generations.

Under the microscope, the shells and skeletons of microfossils
show infinite variations of organic form. Among all, foraminifera,
radiolaria, diatom and coccolithophore are distinct in their
exquisite beauty. That each individual is unique in its originality,
geometry, and architecture leaves us to be deeply awed by the
natural wonders.

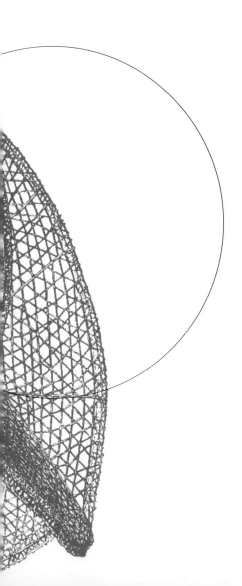

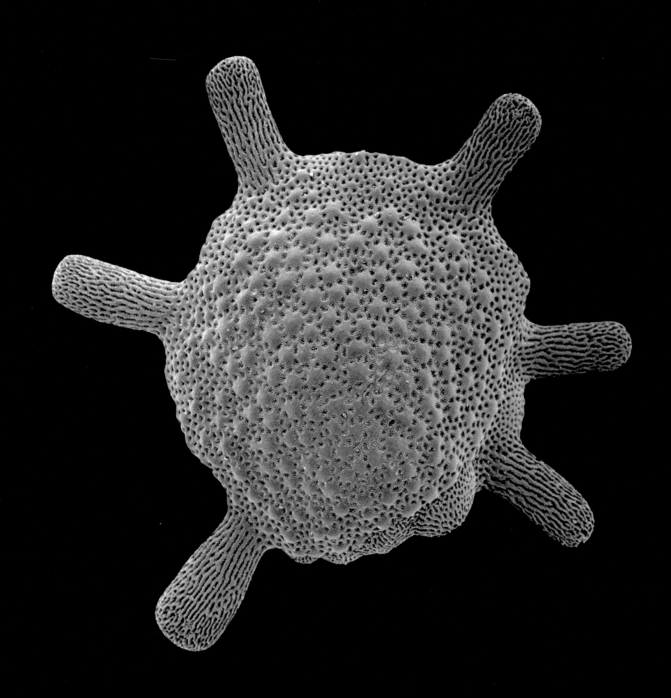

1

有孔蟲
Foraminifera

有孔蟲為單細胞原生生物，擅於建造不同造型的外殼，有的構造簡單，僅具一個房室；有的擁有多個房室，新房室依序排列成長串，或螺旋盤繞。原生質大多聚集於殼內，各房室以一個或多個開口相通，網狀偽足由此伸出捕食，有孔蟲之名即出自殼體具有孔洞該一特徵。

有孔蟲絕大多數生活於海洋，現生種類可達四千種之多。底棲性有孔蟲在海底或海藻上緩慢移動，少數固定生長，從潮間帶到海溝深處都可見其身影；廣泛分布於海洋上層的浮游性有孔蟲，種類雖只有數十種，死後殼體沉落海底，成為鈣質軟泥的主要組成。

Foraminifera are a group of single-celled organisms, and are expert in building shells of various styles. The shells are commonly divided into chambers that are added during growth, though the simplest forms are open tubes or hollow spheres. The protoplasm is largely enclosed within a hard shell. They catch their food with a network of thin pseudopodia that extend from apertures in the shell. Foraminifera are named after this feature of having connected hole through the wall between each chamber.

Foraminifera are found in all marine environments, they may be planktonic or benthic in mode of life. There are an estimated 4,000 species living in the world's oceans today. Benthic foraminifera move slowly on algae or on the seafloor. They can be found from intertidal to the deepest ocean trenches. Planktonic foraminifera, with only a dozen species, are widely distributed in the upper part of ocean. After death, they sink to the seafloor and constitute as the main component of calcareous ooze.

有孔蟲（法屬南方與南極領地，2017 年）
Foraminifera (French Southern and Antarctic Lands, 2017)

Kingdom Rhizaria　有孔蟲界
　Phylum Foraminifera　有孔蟲門
　　Class Globothalamea　球房蟲綱
　　　Order Rotaliida　輪蟲目
　　　　Family Globigerinidae　抱球蟲科
　　　　　Genus *Turborotalita*　抱球蟲屬
　　　　　　Turborotalita quinqueloba　五葉抱球蟲

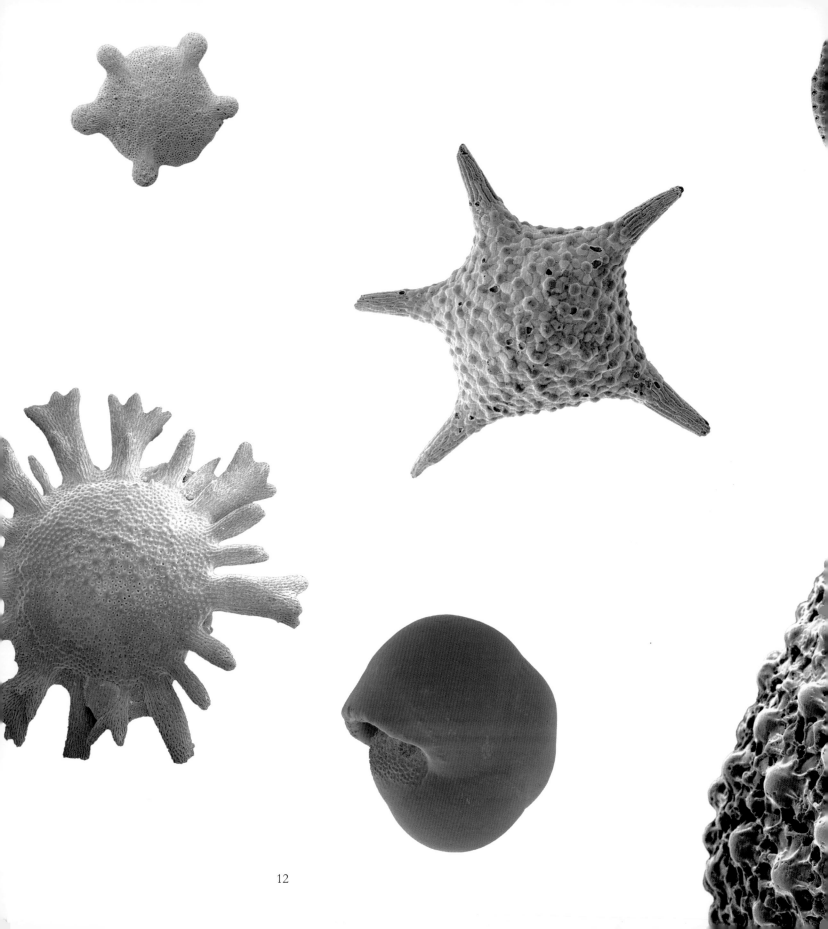

有孔蟲的形態多樣性
Morphological Diversity in Foraminifera

猶如靈活應變的建築師，有孔蟲善於運用環境周遭不同材料構築外殼，能因地制宜。有的便宜行事，只有一層有機質外殼，難以保存為化石；有的就地取材，分泌有機質內襯以黏附砂礫或生物碎屑；但多數能分泌碳酸鈣外殼，饒富巧思地陸續增建新房室，其外型與排列遂成為有孔蟲主要分類依據，若再考量口孔、外表殼飾等細節來加以鑑別，已命名的化石與現生屬種可達四萬多種。

Like a flexible architect, foraminifera utilize available materials to build their tests. Some resolve to the simplicity of building one layer of organic wall, which rarely preserved as fossils; some secrete organic cements to agglutinate fine sands and biological debris; but most of them construct carbonate shells of different types. The morphology of foraminiferal shells varies enormously. These shells are classified primarily on the wall composition and chamber arrangement. If we take into account the subtle features of aperture and sculpture, the total number of recorded fossil and recent foraminifera is over 40,000 species.

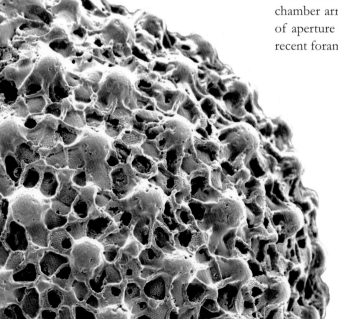

Drawn & Engraved.

REFERENCE

		feet				feet				feet				feet				feet
1	Pyramid of Cheops	479	6	Porcelain Tower, Nankin	414	11	Square Tower, Bologna	354	16	York Minster	230	21	Leaning Tower, Pisa	187
2	Antwerp Cathedral	472	7	Salisbury Cathedral	410	12	Pantheon, Paris	261	17	Westminster Abbey	225	22	Nelson's Monument, London	176
3	Strasburg Cathedral	466	8	St Pauls, London	404	13	Kuttub Minor, Hindoostan	258	18	St Sophia, Constantinople	210	23	Colosseum, Rome	161
4	St Ettienne, Vienna	460	9	Victoria Tower, Do	400	14	Bow Church, London	235	19	Monument, London	202	24	Pont du Gard, France	153
5	St Peters, Rome	434	10	Hotel de Ville, Brussels	355	15	Canterbury Cathedral	235	20	Scotts Mont, Edinburgh	200	25	Arc de Triomphe, Paris	144

London, Published by James Reynolds, 174 Strand, March 30, 1850.

金字塔的建築師
The Architect of Pyramid

早在 1889 年巴黎艾菲爾鐵塔完工之前，埃及古夫金字塔就已蟬聯人造最高建築的紀錄近四千年之久。這一方方堆砌成金字塔的巨石，來自吉薩附近採石場開採的石灰岩。仔細端詳石塊斷面，仍能見到扁豆狀的化石散置其間，這些大型有孔蟲以貨幣石為主，於古地中海溫暖的淺海水域中生活，生存年代距今約三千五百萬年前。

Before the construction of the Eiffel Tower was finished in 1889, the Khufu pyramid of Egypt had been held the title of the man-made tallest structure for four thousand years. The pyramid's limestone blocks were from the quarries near Giza. Upon close examination, lentils-shape fossils scattered over the surfaces of these blocks could be found. These carbonate rocks are constituted by the large benthic foraminifer Nummulites, which lived in sunlit and warm waters of the Mediterranean Sea dating back to approximately 35 million years ago.

微化石美術館 Museum of Microfossil

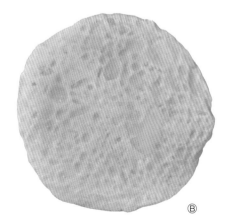

Ⓐ 十九世紀人造建物高度世界之最（1850 年出版）
The tallest man-made building in the world in 19th century (published in 1850)

Ⓑ 貨幣石

產地：法雅姆，埃及｜年代：始新世
Nummulite **sp.**
Location: El Fayum, Egypt｜Age: Eocene

15

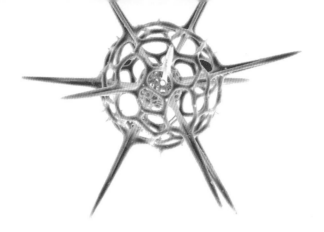

Kingdom Rhizaria　有孔蟲界
Phylum Radiozoa　放射蟲門
Class Polycystina　多囊蟲綱
Order Nassellaria　罩籠蟲目
Family Theoperidae　裙籠蟲科
Genus *Pterocanium*　翼籃蟲屬
Pterocanium tricolpum　長腳翼籃蟲

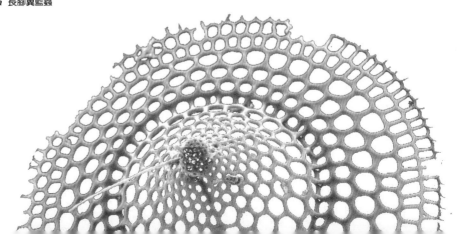

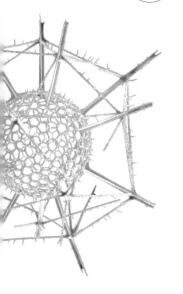

放射蟲
Radiolaria

放射蟲擁有精巧細緻的骨架,整體結構呈現輻射對稱的幾何造型,常被藝術家或設計師運用在各自的創作中。放射蟲與有孔蟲同是原生生物,原生質儲放在中心囊,軸狀偽足或絲狀偽足由此伸出,矽質骨架是由細胞膜分泌矽膠後,再由偽足協助建造而成,每一個體都獨具美感。

放射蟲全都是浮游於大洋的居民,行獨居或群居性生活。在熱帶海洋上層水體較為豐富,也有生活在不見陽光的深水類型,可能與體內共生藻的存在與否相關。現生種總數估計在 700 至 1,000 種之間。

With their glassy skeletons of radial symmetry and geometric form, radiolaria are among the most stunning beauty of all protists. The delicate skeletons form a porous lattice of variable morphology. The striking characteristics of these organisms inspire many designers in their artwork. The central capsule divides the cell into the inner and outer portions of endoplasm and ectoplasm. Radiolarian skeletons are made of opaline silica, which originated from siliceous gel deposited within a thin cytoplasmic sheath. Each entity has its unique elegance.

Radiolaria are solitary or colonial marine plankton. They appear to be most abundant in warm waters of the equatorial zone. Total diversity declines as latitude increases. Besides water temperature and salinity, there is evidence that maximum abundances of radiolaria below the surface are associated with maximum concentrations of chlorophyll. Total number of living species is estimated to lie between 700 and 1,000.

©

Ⓐ 放射蟲（塞內加爾，1972 年）
   Radiolaria (Senegal, 1972)

Ⓑ 放射蟲（德國，2016 年）
   Radiolaria (Germany, 2016)

Ⓒ 放射蟲模型
   Radiolaria model

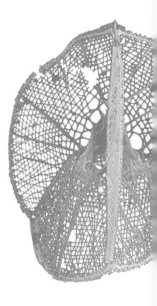

17

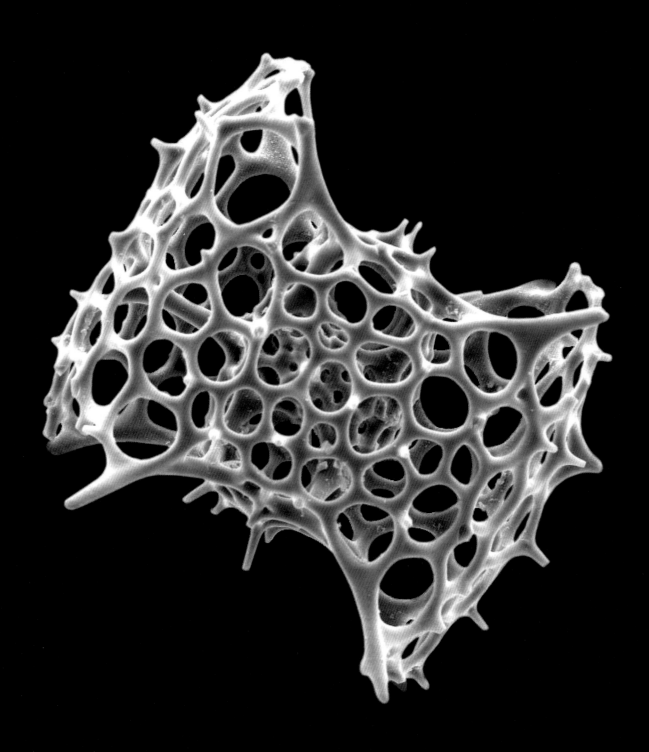

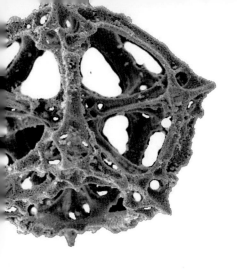

放射蟲的形態多樣性
Morphological Diversity in Radiolaria

依照骨架型態和結構的對稱關係，常見的放射蟲分為泡沫蟲和罩籠蟲兩大類。多軸對稱的泡沫蟲，以幾何格子築成層狀的球型構造，並以數根骨刺串連成一體；至於單軸對稱的罩籠蟲，一般呈狹長的圓錐狀構造，中心囊的外型也不同。

此外，依據穿孔的大小和型態，棘刺的大小和排列，隔壁的數目和厚度，外牆的結構，內部球體的特點，可作為放射蟲屬種層級的細部指引。

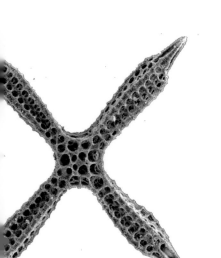

According to the morphology and geometry of the skeletons, radiolaria are subdivided into two groups: Spumellaria and Nassellaria. The former possesses a spherical lattice of multiple axes symmetry, with several concentric shells bearing spines and supporting bars. As for the latter, it has uniaxial symmetry and is usually in an elongated conical, with a different shape of the central capsule.

Detailed features of skeletal structure could be useful to classification at generic and specific levels, which include the size and shape of the pores, the size and arrangement of the spines, the number and thickness of the bars and beams, the structure of the cortical shells, and the characteristics of the medullary shells.

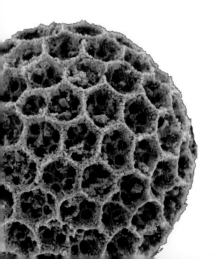

LA PORTE MONUMENTALE DE LA PLACE DE LA CONCORDE

1900 年巴黎萬國博覽會入口主體建築（1900 年出版）
The main gate of the 1900 World Fair in Paris
(published in 1900)

新藝術運動的謬思
The Muse of Art Nouveau

二十世紀之初，歐洲興起了新藝術運動，這股崇尚自然形式與繁複結構的潮流也反映在建築設計，造型獨特多變、極富結構層次的放射蟲成為師法對象。法國建築師比奈擔綱設計 1900 年法國萬國博覽會的主體入口建築，他從海克爾繪製的放射蟲汲取創作靈感，這座具有放射蟲的特徵的建築，充分實踐了微物造型之美。

At the beginning of the 20th century, Art Nouveau emerged in Europe. The new art movement is characterized by its use of natural forms and structures in decorative art. The sophisticated morphology of radiolarian skeleton has since become a muse of artists and designers. The French architect René Binet adopted Haeckel's illustrations as an inspiration for the Monumental Gate of the 1900 World Fair in Paris. This huge metal entrance of organic architecture witnessed the naturalistic element in ornamentation.

矽藻
Diatom

Ⓓ

Ⓐ

Ⓑ

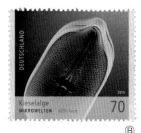

Ⓒ

矽藻顧名思義就是一種具有矽質細胞壁的單細胞藻類，但堆積在細胞壁上不是元素矽，而是二氧化矽膠體型態的蛋白石。因此擁有蛋白石細胞壁的矽藻，在光學顯微鏡下就像一間間形狀不一的玻璃屋。

矽藻大多數水生，幾乎所有水體都能生長。大洋中廣泛分布，喜好高緯度海域的低溫環境，赤道湧升流區產量也較豐富。矽藻生活方式有被動漂浮和自發運動，也有營固著他物生活者。

As its Chinese name implies, diatom is a kind of unicellular algae with a siliceous cell wall. However, what accumulates on the cell wall is not silicon, but amorphous hydrated silica (opal). Under the optical microscope, the opaline cell walls sparkle like glass houses with incredible styles.

Diatoms occupy almost every aquatic environments, thriving in ponds, lakes, rivers, lagoons, and oceanic waters. Widely distributed in the open ocean, they prefer the low-temperature high-nutrient waters at high latitudes, while high primary production is also found in equatorial upwelling areas. Diatoms most commonly suspend in water, although they can attach to substrates as well.

微化石美術館 Museum of Microfossil

Kingdom Chromista 原藻界
Phylum Ochrophyta 褐藻門
Class Bacillariophyceae 矽藻綱
Order Corethrales 圓篩藻目
Family Corethraceae 圓篩藻科
Genus *Corethron* 毛藻屬
Corethron criophilum 小環毛藻

Ⓐ **矽藻**（法屬南方與南極領地，2016 年）
　　Diatom (France Southern and Antarctic Lands, 2016)

Ⓑ **矽藻**（德國，2015 年）
　　Diatom (Germany, 2015)

Ⓒ **矽藻**（英屬南極領地，1984 年）
　　Diatom (British Antarctic Territory, 1984)

Ⓓ **矽藻土**
　　Diatomite

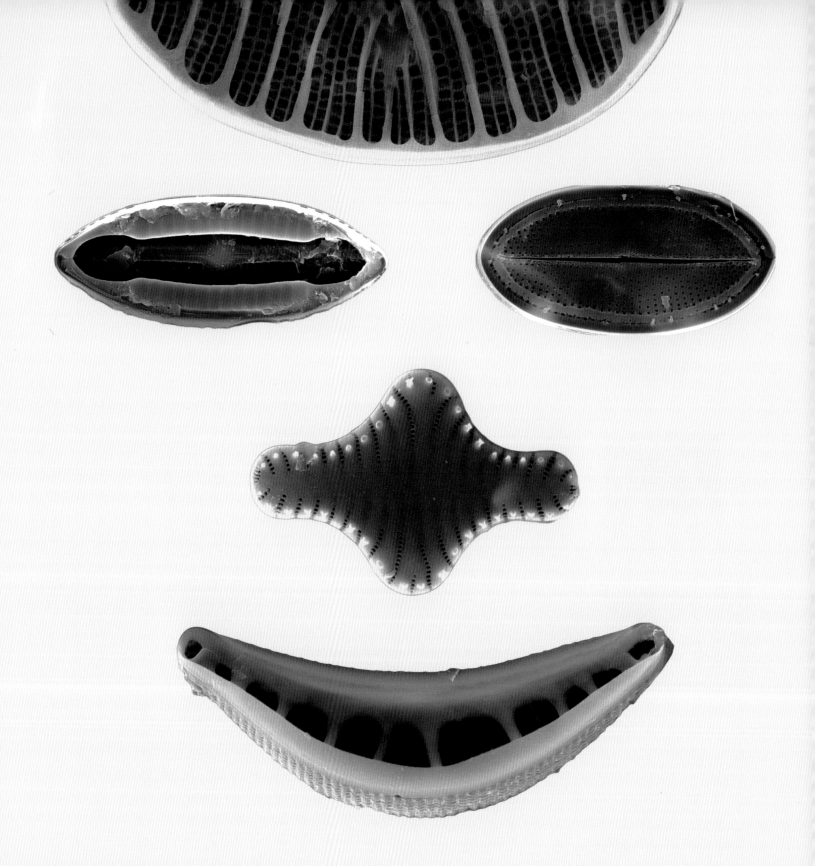

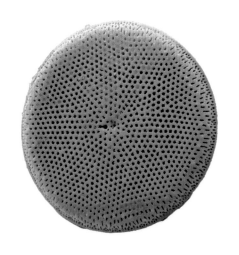

矽藻的形態多樣性
Morphological Diversity in Diatom

矽藻殼壁千姿百態，有圓形、三角形、五角形、長橢圓形等，但其基本結構是由兩個大小不一的殼片相互套合而成。矽藻主要依據殼面的特徵進行種屬判斷，根據其殼片幾何對稱可分成兩大類，分別是放射型對稱的中心矽藻，與兩側對稱的羽紋矽藻。

電子顯微鏡的觀察，將矽藻殼面凹孔排列成各種紋飾的變化加以確認，而殼縫的有無、位置和型態，又可將羽紋矽藻分為無殼縫型、單殼縫型、雙殼縫型、短殼縫型與管殼縫型。

Frustule is the hard and porous external layer of diatoms. It is composed of two identically shaped valves. One of the valves is slightly larger than the other, so as to allow one valve to fit inside the edge of the other. Diatoms are divided into two groups according to the frustule structure. Centric diatoms are radially symmetrically, while pennate diatoms are bilaterally symmetric.

Under a scanning electron microscope, the siliceous wall can be highly patterned with a variety of pores, ribs, minute spines, marginal ridges and elevations. The characteristics can be used to divide pennate diatoms further into araphid, monoraphid, biraphid, eunotioid and epithemioid.

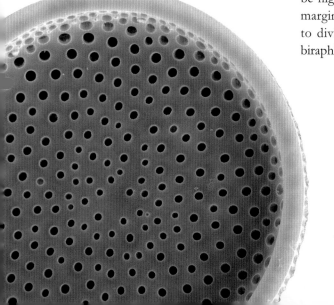

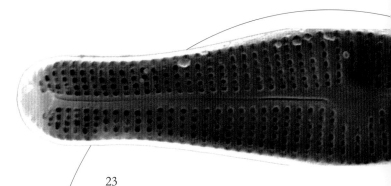

23

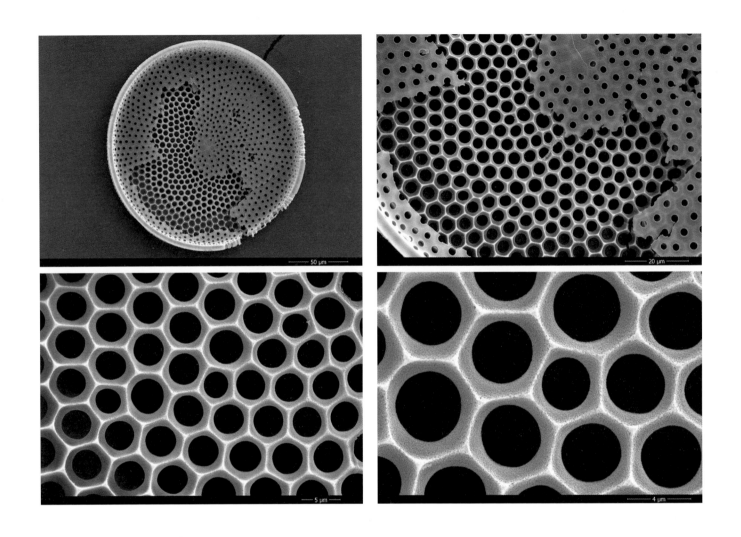

高倍率放大的矽藻微細構造（1. 1550 倍；2. 4000 倍；3. 10000 倍；4. 20000 倍）

Diatom's ultrastructure under high power magnification (1. x1550; 2. x4000; 3. x10000; 4. x20000)

奈米科技的新典範
The New Paradigm of Nanotechnology

矽藻殼壁之上所見大小均一，排列有序的孔洞，是人類目前仍無法成功製造的矽晶產品，成為仿生科技最佳學習對象。矽藻僅需合適的陽光和營養鹽就能大量增生，猶如品管嚴格的生產線，能達到高效率、高良率的工業標準；矽藻藉由生物礦化形成矽質外殼，在一般常溫的條件下就能生長，而非動輒數百度的高溫，這些優點都是科技產業追求的目標。

The porous structures with intricate patterns in diatom shells are among the most remarkable examples of biological nanofabrication. Since the biosilica nanopatterns are precisely reproduced in a species-specific manner, a genetic control of this biomineralization process has been regarded as a paradigm for controlled production of nanostructured silica. Diatoms need only moderate sunlight and nutrients to proliferate. Working like a strict production line, diatoms can multiply efficiently and rapidly. Silica–based materials have been conventionally made at very high temperature, while biogenic silica is made under room temperature. Such advantages are the goals pursued by the leading high–tech industry.

4

鈣板藻
Coccolithophore

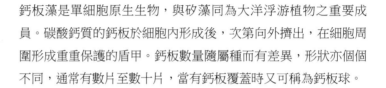

鈣板藻是單細胞原生生物，與矽藻同為大洋浮游植物之重要成員。碳酸鈣質的鈣板於細胞內形成後，次第向外擠出，在細胞周圍形成重重保護的盾甲。鈣板數量隨屬種而有差異，形狀亦個個不同，通常有數片至數十片，當有鈣板覆蓋時又可稱為鈣板球。

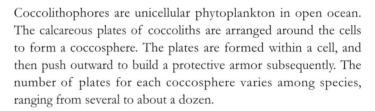

生活於海洋透光帶的鈣板藻，老化或成為浮游動物吞食後所排出的糞粒，從海洋透光層下沉時，因純白的碳酸鈣質地，狀似海洋下雪一般，緩慢飄落至海底，形成鈣質軟泥。

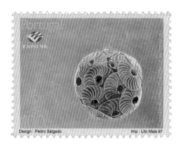

鈣板藻（葡萄牙‧1997 年）
Coccolithophore (Portugal, 1997)

Kingdom Chromista 原藻界
Phylum Haptophyta 定鞭藻門
Class Pyrmnesiophyceae 定鞭藻綱
Order Coccolithales 顆石藻目
Family Calcidiscaceae 鈣板藻科
Genus *Calcidiscus* 鈣板藻屬
Calcidiscus leptoporus 細孔鈣板藻

Coccolithophores are unicellular phytoplankton in open ocean. The calcareous plates of coccoliths are arranged around the cells to form a coccosphere. The plates are formed within a cell, and then push outward to build a protective armor subsequently. The number of plates for each coccosphere varies among species, ranging from several to about a dozen.

Coccolithphores live in the photic zone of upper ocean where the sunlight can reach. After death, these snowflake-like particles settle slowly to the sea floor as the calcareous ooze. The fine particles can also repackaged within a fecal pellet of zooplanktons. In this way, coccoliths can reach ocean floor at a higher speed.

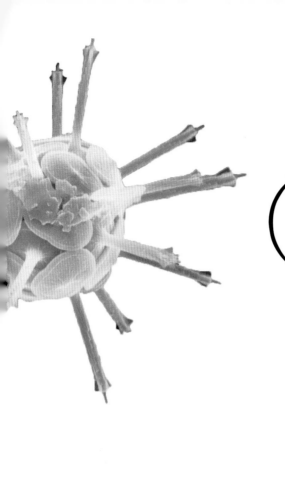
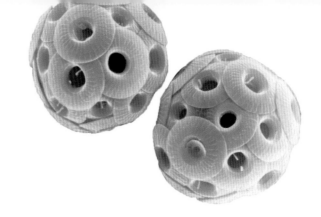

鈣板藻的形態多樣性
Morphological Diversity in Coccolithophore

現生鈣板藻主要有兩種鈣板組成方式，全顆石和異顆石。全顆石全由菱形體的方解石構成，排列規則，脫落後幾乎全數破裂分解；異顆石往往較大，由不同次構件組成，形成堅固持久的結構，能保存為微化石。

散落於海床之上的鈣板藻，通常是以個別分散的鈣板形式存在於鈣質軟泥。鈣板藻分類都是依據鈣板的特徵進行屬種判斷，由異顆石所成的鈣板有片盤狀、花籃狀、圓形、橢圓形、棒狀、四邊形等，形狀和構造變化多端。

There are two basic modes of coccolith construction, holococcoliths and heterococcoliths. Holococcoliths consist of regularly arranged rhombohedral calcite. They usually disintegrate and dissolve after they are shed. Heterococcoliths are usually larger and build of several submicroscopic elements, combined together into a relatively rigid structure. It is the heterococcoliths that provide the bulk of the microfossil record.

After death coccolithophores sink through the water column and tend to disaggregate into dispersed coccoliths. The heterococcoliths eventually fall to the ocean floor to constitute calcareous ooze. Coccolith morphology is the basis for classification of both living and fossil members of the group. They exhibit incredible variety of morphology, namely disc, basket, round, oval, rod, and quadrilateral.

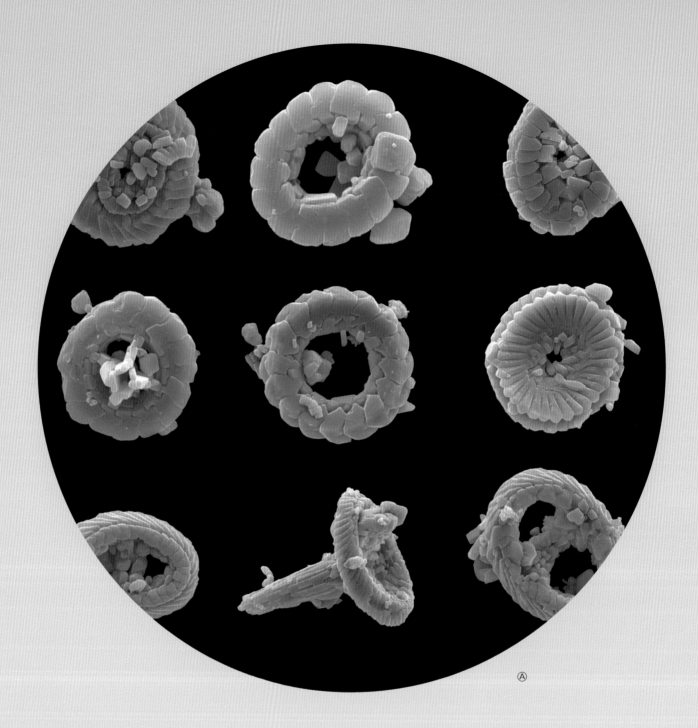

Ⓐ

Ⓐ 電子顯微鏡下觀察白堊所呈現的各類超微化石
   Nannofossils in chalk under the electron microscope

Ⓑ 多佛白崖（英國‧2012 年）
   White Cliffs of Dover (England, 2012)

Ⓒ 多佛港附近以綿延的白崖為當地獨特地景
   The White Cliffs of Dover gains worldwide fame for its unique landscape

Ⓓ 白堊岩
   產地：英國多佛 ｜ 年代：白堊紀
   Chalk
   Location: Dover, England ｜ Age: Cretaceous

白堊紀的無名推手
The Invisible Founders of the Cretaceous

白堊紀為中生代最後一個時期，其名稱源自該時期獨特的產物。白堊係鈣板藻為主的生物源沉積物，原本生活在海洋表層透光海域中的鈣板藻，死亡後沉降至海底，以長達數百萬年的時間持續累積，形成巨厚而獨具特色的地質景觀，廣泛分布於英吉利海峽兩側，從英國東南部的多佛，到法國西北部的諾曼第，都可見到壯觀的白色海崖。

ⓑ

The Cretaceous is the last chronologic unit of the Mesozoic, bearing the name from its unique rock type. Chalk originated from pelagic sediments is composed predominantly of coccolithophores. The calcareous sediments were deposited very slowly, probably half a millimeter a year, equivalent to about 180 coccoliths piled one on top of another. A finely grained pure limestone layer with a thickness up to 500 meters might be deposited over millions of years. The spectacular white cliffs are widely distributed on both sides of the English Channel, from the coastline of the Dover in UK to the Normandy in France.

ⓒ

ⓓ

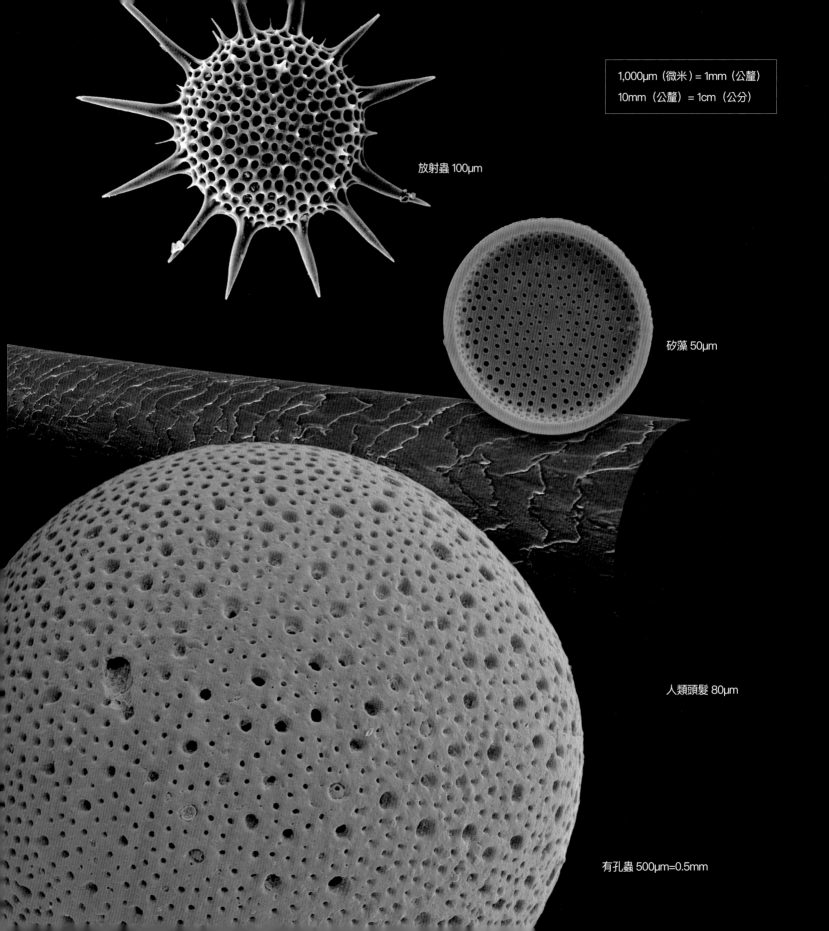

放射蟲 100μm

1,000μm（微米）= 1mm（公釐）
10mm（公釐）= 1cm（公分）

矽藻 50μm

人類頭髮 80μm

有孔蟲 500μm=0.5mm

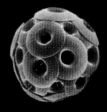

鈣板藻 10μm

微化石隱身術

The Stealth Techniques of Microfossil

人類肉眼難以辨識的微體化石，個體通常在一公釐以下，必須仰賴顯微鏡進行鑑定。不同類別的平均體型差異懸殊，有孔蟲與放射蟲如同細沙，大小通常在數百微米；鈣板藻則如飄揚空中的微塵，單一鈣板甚至不到十微米，稱之超微化石。若把微體化石一個個緊挨著排放，一公釐就可並置好幾個有孔蟲或放射蟲，甚至可以擺放近百個鈣板藻。

Microfossils are generally smaller than 1 mm in size and hard to discernible with naked eye. The most common sizes between different groups vary significantly. Foraminifera and radiolarian are as large as fine sands, which have a typical size range of 100~1,000 μ m. Coccolithophore is like a dust floating in the air. A single grain of coccolith is even less than 10 μ m, which is near the limit of resolution of a light microscope. Microfossil smaller than 63 μ m in diameter can be further referred to nannofossil. If microfossils are lined up tightly in a row, you may count 5 to 10 bugs of foraminifera or radiolarian, and even 100 coccolithophores or so within 1mm in length.

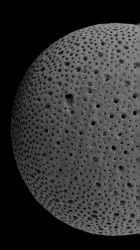

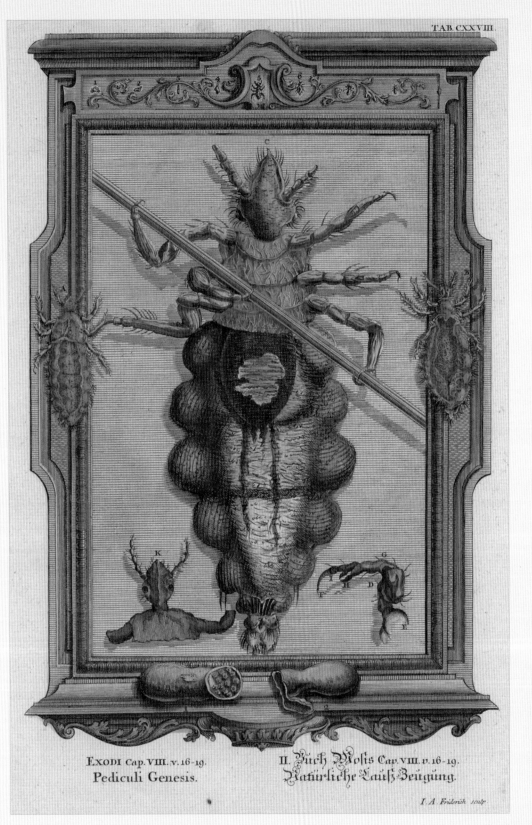

TAB. CXXVIII.

EXODI Cap. VIII. v. 16-19.
Pediculi Genesis.

II. Buch Moses Cap. VIII. v. 16-19.
Natürliche Laus-Zeugung.

I. A. Friderich sculp.

體蝨（銅版印刷，1731-1735 年出版）
出自舍希策爾出版的《神聖的物理》，抓附
毛髮的體蝨翻刻自虎克 1665 年出版的《顯
微圖譜》。

Louse (Engraved printing; published in
1731-1735)
From Johann Jakob Scheuchzer's book
Physica Sacra, the louse was originated from
Hooke's *Micrographa* published in 1665.

2

微化石的藝術與科學
Art and Science of
Microfossil

"
藉由顯微鏡之助，再細小之物皆纖毫畢現，全新的視覺經驗拓
展了對微美幻境的認知。

*By the help of microscopes, there is nothing so small, as to escape
our inquiry; hence there is a new visible world discovered to the
understanding.*

"

—— 虎克 (*Robert Hooke, 1635 - 1703*)

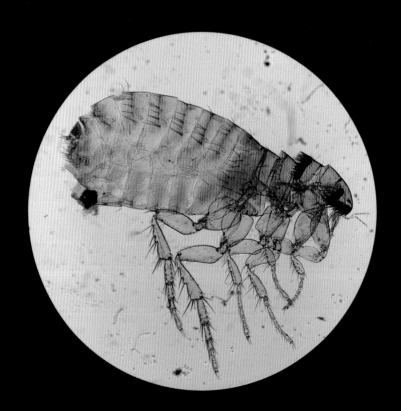

早在十七世紀顯微鏡發明之初，虎克就曾經以有孔蟲作為觀察對象，使用放大倍率猶勝一籌的雷文霍克，甚至有矽藻的觀察記錄，人類造訪顯微世界的視覺印象，如今猶可透過作為科學插圖的版畫窺其面貌。

這些版畫以細膩線條將微小生物躍然呈現於紙頁，看起來既寫實卻又奇幻，透過博物學家、畫家、鎸版師攜手合作，版畫提供世人對於微美幻境的無限遐想。

As early as the invention of the microscope in the 17th century, the first published illustration of foraminifera was documented from the text of the *Micrographia* by Robert Hooke. Anthonie van Leeuwenhoek had described the observations of diatoms using single lens microscope of even greater magnifying power. Through the scientific illustration of engraving prints, the impressive images that human being encountered the microscopic world can still be seen intact.

These magnified engravings demonstrate that the tiny creatures seem vividly on paper with delicate touches, seemingly realistic and marvelous simultaneously. Through the collaboration of naturalists, painters and engravers, everyone can be inspired by the exquisite beauty of the prints.

跳蚤顯微玻片及放大影像（J. Bourgogne 製備，19 世紀中葉）

Microscopic slide of a flea with enlarged image (mid-19th century)

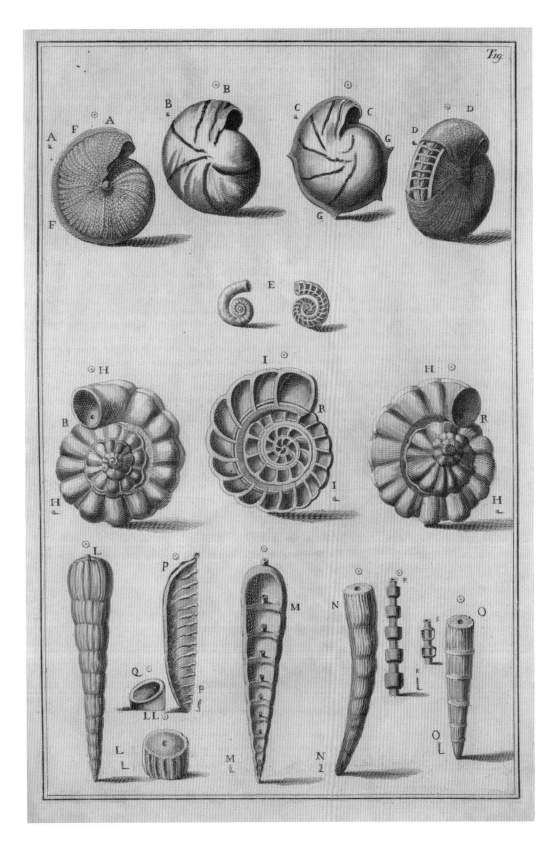

有孔蟲（銅版印刷，1742 年出版）

Niccolo Gualtieri 出版的貝類圖鑑包含後來才分類為 "有孔蟲" 的圖版，圖上每一個放大的有孔蟲旁邊也畫出句號般大小的實際尺寸來做參考比例。

Foraminifera (Engraved printing; published in 1742)

An illustration of the Niccolo Gualtieri's conchology contained seashells which were later named "foraminifera". The actual size was plotted next to each enlarged foraminifera to scale.

1

微化石初登場
The Microfossil's Debug

貝殼以其型態多元色彩繽紛，是十八世紀博物館從大自然之中獵奇蒐集的主要對象之一。辨識鑑別各式大小不一的貝類，勢必留意到同樣形成精巧外殼的有孔蟲。

這些必須放在顯微鏡下辨識的精緻殼體，隨著個體成長建造新房室，許多種類呈現如同鸚鵡螺般等角螺線的生長模式，學者曾因此將有孔蟲分類錯誤地放置在軟體動物頭足類之下。

Molluscan shells, with their distinct shapes and multifarious patterns, came to form the basic collections in the cabinet of curiosities of the 18th century, an early ancestor of the modern natural history museum. To classify molluscan shells with various sizes, morphologies and characteristics, the intricate foraminiferal shells have also been noticed.

Foraminifera can only be identified properly under the microscope. New chamber is added subsequently as its growth. The spiral shells of the foraminifera closely resemble the shells of Nautilus, and the latter are the model examples of the logarithmic spiral. The visual similarity of appearance has led some scholars to erroneously place these tiny shells as the Cephalopodes microscopiques.

菊石版畫（銅版印刷，1731-1735 年出版）

菊石是中生代即已滅絕的物種，長久以來被臆測為超大型有孔蟲，直到十九世紀才普遍接受為頭足類的一員。

Ammonites (Engraved printing; published in 1731-1735)

Ammonite, an extinct species at the end of the Mesozoic, has long been considered to be a giant foraminifera. It was not universally recongined as a group of cephalopods until the 19th century.

英國貝類圖鑑（1828 年出版）

直到十九世紀初，貝殼圖鑑仍將有孔蟲分類放置在鸚鵡螺的頭足類之下。

British Concology Catalogue (published in 1828)

The British shell catalog still places the classification of foraminifera under Cephalopoda of Nautilina.

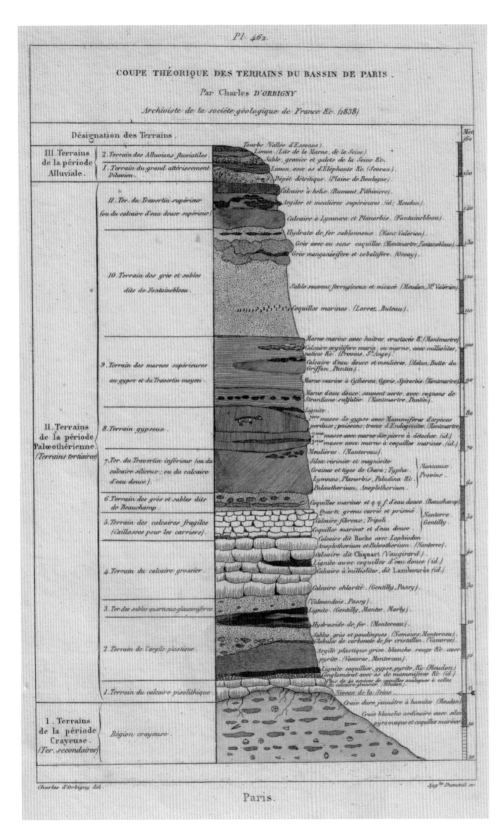

巴黎盆地新生代地層剖面（1835 年出版）

Stratigraphic profile of the Paris basin
(published in 1835)

40

微體古生物學的開創

Pioneer of Micropaleontology

對於有孔蟲分類奠定開創性基礎，被譽為微體古生物學之父的道比尼，起初也承襲著這個見解，直到杜甲登發現有孔蟲擁有原生生物的特質，方才察覺這個錯誤。道比尼於 1853 年擔任法國自然史博物館首任古生物學講座，除了於海濱採集現生有孔蟲，進行系統性的有孔蟲分類之外，也從巴黎盆地不同年代的地層採集，探討有孔蟲在生物地層學方面之應用。

Alcide d'Orbigny, the father of micropaleontology, and a founder for the classification of foraminifera, adopted at first the conventional view that foraminifera were microscopic cephalopods. It was not until Félix Dujardin observed the distinct characteristics of protozoa that d'Orbigny was convinced to recognize his mistake. In 1853, he was nominated by the French National Museum of Natural History as the chair of paleontology in his honor. He took a systematic classification of the living foraminifera at the seashore, and the fossils from the strata of different ages in the Paris Basin, to explore their applications in biostratigraphy.

阿爾西德·道比尼（1802-1857）

玻利維亞 2002 年發行道比尼郵票。道比尼年輕時前往巴黎即因為有孔蟲的研究出色而受到重視，隨後前往南美進行長達八年的野外採集。

Alcide d'Orbigny (1802-1857)

In 2002, Bolivia issued the d'Orbigny stamp. He traveled to Paris in his youth, and was caught attention because of his outstanding research on foraminifera. Afterwards, he went to South America for eight years to collect samples.

微化石的藝術與科學　Art and Science of Microfossil

Ⓐ 十八世紀末英式複合式單眼顯微鏡

English compound monocular microscope in the second half of the 18th century

Ⓑ 顯微玻片製備工具

Microscope slide preparation accessory cabinet

Ⓒ 十九世紀英國複合式雙眼顯微鏡

Compound biocular microscope in the 19th century

2

微觀自然的美學時尚
Art and Fashion of the Microcosm

維多利亞女王在位期間正值十九世紀工業革命蓬勃之際，國力鼎盛的大英帝國扶持了新興的中產階級，造成社會結構的重大改變，科學素養遂成為文明教養的重要指標。

這股崇尚科學的時代氛圍同樣影響至個人生活層面，引領知識份子親近自然領略造物神奇，許多專書出版介紹顯微鏡操作與薄片製作，探索感官視覺未及的微型小宇宙。

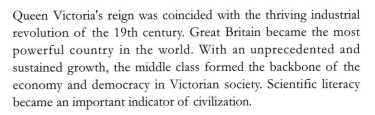

Queen Victoria's reign was coincided with the thriving industrial revolution of the 19th century. Great Britain became the most powerful country in the world. With an unprecedented and sustained growth, the middle class formed the backbone of the economy and democracy in Victorian society. Scientific literacy became an important indicator of civilization.

During the Victorian era, the passion for science influenced the leisure pursuits of individual life. It encourages people to get in touch with nature and to appreciate the natural wonders. Many popular science books were published to disperse the knowledge of the microscope operations and slide preparations. With the help of the microscope, everyone can explore the invisible microcosm.

©

維多利亞時期的顯微玻片
The Victorian Microscopic Slides

隨著自然觀察的風氣漸開，取材多元、別出心裁的各類顯微玻片因應收藏需求蓬勃而生，來自海洋深處的微化石也成為時尚新寵，顯微玻片從而成為拓展視覺感官與知性認知的新興收藏。

這些留存至今超過百年的維多利亞時期玻片，一方方彷若封印往昔歲月的時空膠囊。部分外觀包覆一層用色典雅印有圖案的紙質外衣，這些設計出眾的包裝，印有製造者的識別商標，提供可供辨識製作商家與年代的重要參考。

As the natural observation became a popular culture phenomenon, ingenious microscopic slides had thus been prepared to satisfy the curiosities of the collectors. Marine microfossil caught attention for its exquisite beauty. Slides mounted with novel objects could be used to expand visual sensory and intellectual cognition.

The Victorian slides, retained for more than 100 years, are like the sealing of the time capsule. Some slides are covered either wholly or partly with colorful gilt of lithographed papers. A lot of the outstanding preparer's works are recognizable, as each of them settled on standard paper colors and graphic designs, which became their trademark of sorts.

顯微玻片展示盒
Microscope slide display cabinet

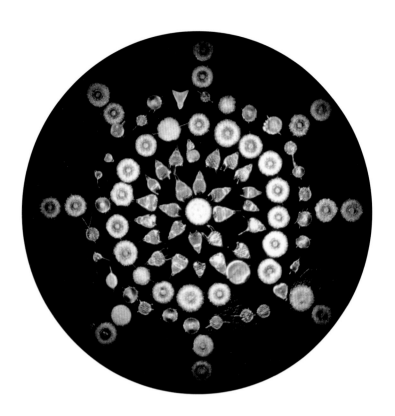

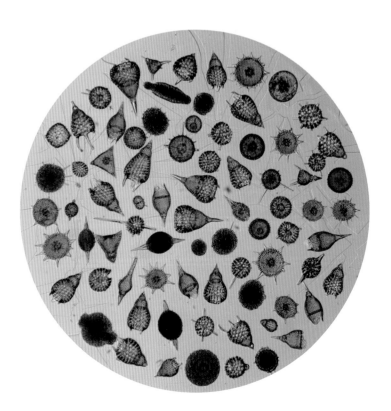

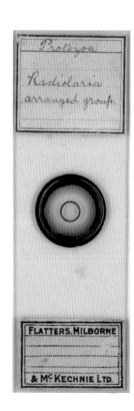

46

顯微鏡下的放射蟲
Radiolaria under Microscope

十九世紀顯微玻片常可見到標示為"Polycystina"者，這個名詞出自德國微生物學家艾倫伯格的命名，他是最早辨識出放射蟲化石的學者，對於矽藻分類也有卓越貢獻。維多利亞時期玻片的放射蟲大多來自加勒比海巴貝多島所產的化石，並非現生於海洋的種類，年代大約距今四千萬年前的始新世至漸新世。

The 19th-century microscopic slides were commonly labeled as "Polycystina", a group of the Radiolarians coined by the German microbiologist, Christian Ehrenberg. He was the first scholar to identify fossil radiolaria, and his contribution to diatom classification was also notable. Most of radiolarian slides in the Victoria period were mounted with fossil specimens from the Barbados in the Caribbean Sea, dated about 40 million years ago between Eocene to Oligocene.

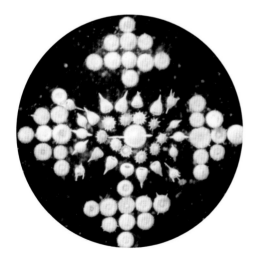

排列成形的放射蟲顯微玻片
Arranged radiolaria on microscope slides

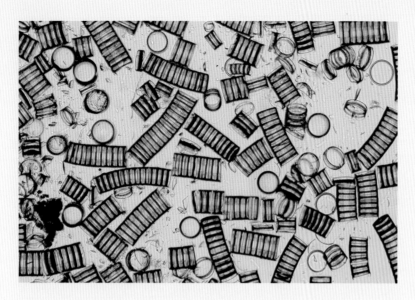

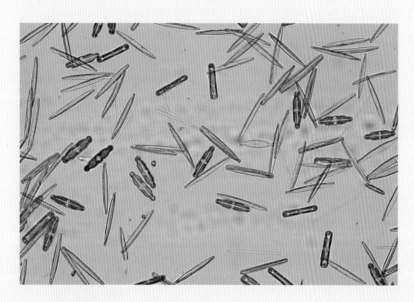

Ⓐ

Ⓐ 矽藻顯微玻片
Diatoms on microscope slides

Ⓑ 排列成形的矽藻顯微玻片
Arranged diatoms on microscope slides

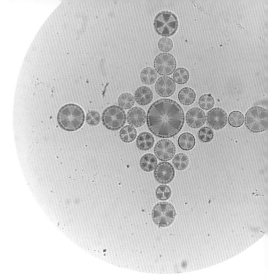

)顯微鏡下的矽藻
Diatom under Microscope

矽藻具有獨特的對稱外型與纖細結構,以其殼體較薄,景深易隨著倍率放大而改變,成為檢視顯微鏡品質的最佳測試物,影像解像力的清晰與否,高下立判。更由於其形態多元,工藝精湛的玻片製造者,甚至將矽藻或以數十,或以上百,逐一排列成特定構圖,肉眼難以辨識的樣本,於高倍率放大後,井然有序的幻化成幾何圖案。

Diatoms exhibit unique symmetrical shapes and intricate structures. Owing to its relatively thin shell, the depth of field is sensitive to magnification changes. So the diatoms were widely used to test the quality and resolution of microscopes. An interesting way of mounting and displaying various diatoms was by selecting and positioning them into groups, usually geometric or patterned arrangements. These arranged slides require the skill and patience one can only image.

Ⓑ

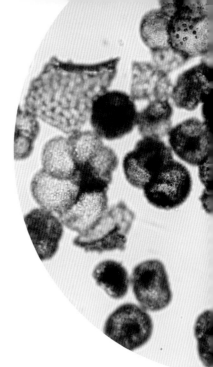

有孔蟲顯微玻片
Foraminifera on microscope slides

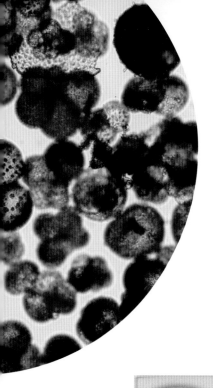

顯微鏡下的有孔蟲
Foraminifera under Microscope

有孔蟲在海洋的分布廣泛，從海灘砂粒到深海底泥都可見到不同種類，以其外型獨特多變，為當時製備玻片常見材料。由於浮游有孔蟲多半生活於開放性大洋環境，少數個體隨波逐流到海濱。一般而言，海灘砂礫所見到的有孔蟲是以底棲有孔蟲為主，深海底泥所見則幾乎都是浮游有孔蟲，依據這個原則，就可與標籤上標示的產地相互印證。

Foraminifera are widely distributed in the oceans, from beach sands to the deep sea muds and therefore, various species can be spotted at different environments. Their shells were the common objects mounted on slides due to their outstanding appearance. As the planktonic foraminifera live in the open ocean, hence, only a few individuals could be drifted to the seashore. In general, the foraminifera collected from the beach sands are mainly benthic, while those found in the deep sea mud are mostly planktonic. Based on this rule, one can check the fauna assemblage with the collected information on the label.

微化石的藝術與科學　Art and Science of Microfossil

VII.

維多利亞時期的顯微圖鑑
Victorian Microscopic Catalogue

伴隨顯微鏡使用人口的增加，顯微玻片專業製備以及銷售通路應運而生，選用的題材包羅萬象，許多暢銷的顯微觀察入門書相繼推出，附有精心繪製的鑑定圖版，許多原本僅是單色印刷的線條輪廓，甚至採用手工上色的方法，呈現顯微鏡底下色彩繽紛的世界。提供常見微小生物的拉丁學名與辨識特徵，從淡水湖泊藻類到深海底泥有孔蟲，都是雅好科學之士獵奇蒐集的對象。

As the population of the microscope users increased, the growing commercial demand was met with an increasing diversity of objects of every imaginable sort around the world. Many introductory books on microscopic observation were published with well-illustrated plates. Some monochromatic prints were even hand-colored to demonstrate the colorful microcosm through microscope. The book may also provide the Latin nomenclature and the characteristics of the microorganisms. People can build his own micro-museum by collecting freshwater lake algae or foraminifera in deep sea, and preparing slides by himself.

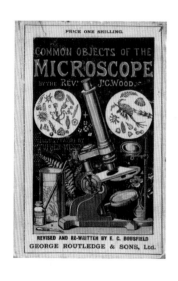

《顯微鏡下常見物》（1861 年出版）
Common Objects of the Microscope
(published in 1861)

微化石的藝術與科學　Art and Science of Microfossil

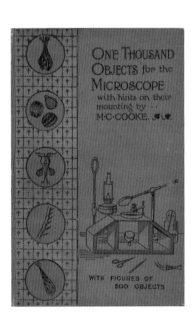

《顯微鏡下常見的一千種物品》（1897年出版）
One Thousand Objects for the Microscope
(published in 1897）

RADIOLARIANS.

1. Rhizosphæra. 2. Sphærozoum. 3. Actinomma. 4. Lithomespilus. 5. Ommato-campe. 6. Carpocanium. 7. Challengeria. 8. Heliosphæra. 9. Clathrocyclas. 10. Dictyophimus.
[*See page* 40.

PLATE IV.

DIATOMS

[*To face p.* 28

微化石的藝術與科學　Art and Science of Microfossil

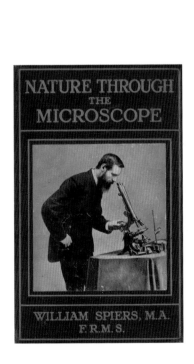

《顯微鏡下的自然觀察》（1909 年出版）

Nature through the Microscope
(published in 1909）

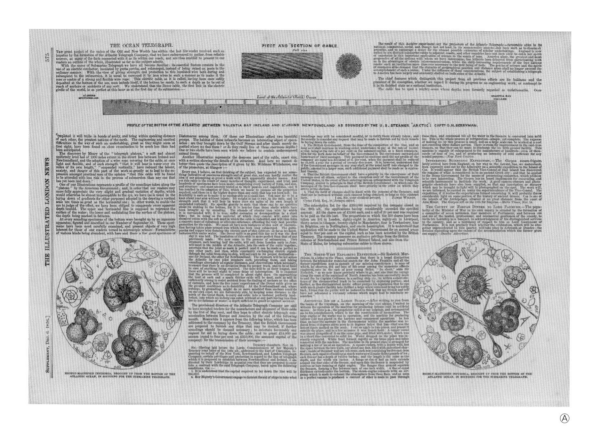

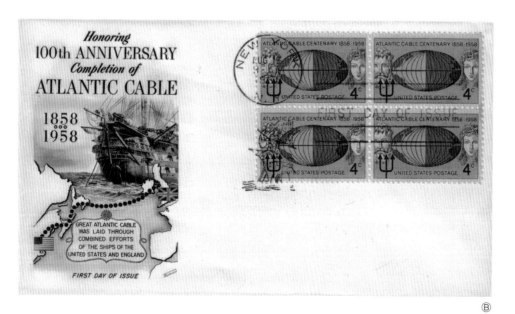

Ⓐ 北大西洋海底沉積物中所發現的微化石
（1856 年發行）

**Microfossils from the sediments of
the North Atlantic** (issued in 1856)

Ⓑ 大西洋海底電纜接通一百周年（美國，
1958 年）

Transatlantic cable 100th anniversary
(USA, 1958)

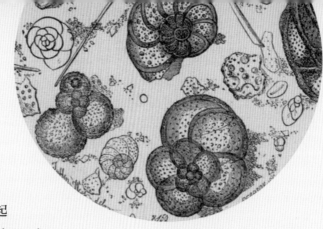

微體古生物學的興起
Rise of the Micropaleontology

直到十九世紀中葉，測量大洋深度仍是極度困難的挑戰，零星的測量多侷限在重要港口與航道，水深很少超過一千公尺。為規劃橫越北大西洋海底電纜的鋪設，1856 年起獨眼巨人號展開海床地形測繪，於東起愛爾蘭西至紐芬蘭的海域進行密集調查，採取海底沉積物，逐漸揭開大洋深處微化石的神祕面紗。

對這項眾所期待的世紀工程，倫敦畫報以大篇幅報導電纜聯接新舊大陸的願景，並描繪深海底泥之中發現的「內太空居民」，外型獨特猶如外星生物的有孔蟲與放射蟲，與我們同樣居住在一個星球之上。

In the middle of the 19th century, depth sounding in open ocean was still a difficult challenge. Sporadic measurements were confined to important seaports and waterways with depths rarely exceeding one thousand meters. For the laying of the first transatlantic telegraph cables, the HMS Cyclops was launched a bathymetric mapping from Ireland to Newfoundland since 1856. Sediments were also collected in this investigation to test the firmness of its bottom. Eventually, the mystery of microfossils in the deep ocean was revealed.

As to the monumental construction of transatlantic cable, a vision of the union of the Old and New Worlds was outlined on *The Illustrated London News*. The report also illustrated the highly-magnified micro-organisms of the inner-space inhabitants, which were mainly composed of foraminifera and radiolaria from the bottom of Atlantic Ocean.

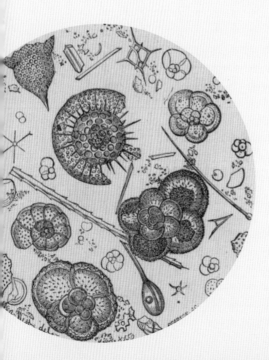

57

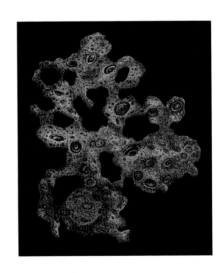

湯瑪斯·赫胥黎（1825-1895）
Thomas Henry Huxley (1825-1895)

海克爾深海蟲
Bathybius haeckelii

鈣板藻的迷思
Myth of the Coccolithophore

赫胥黎輾轉獲得這批來自大西洋底的珍貴樣本，在高倍率的顯微鏡下發現零星的鈣板，成為第一位從海底沉積物辨識出鈣板的科學家。儘管如此，赫胥黎當時並不認為鈣板來自於生物，原因可能是並未發現鈣板球。

1868 年，赫胥黎重新檢視這批保存於酒精的沉積物，發現形如原生質的凝膠狀物質，鈣板零星或是成團的散佈於其間。赫胥黎認為這正是最簡單的生命形式，界於生物與非生物之間的演化失落環節，命名為海克爾深海蟲。然而隨後展開的挑戰者號航次卻未能在深海找到任何佐證，隨船科學家確認該現象出自酒精加入海水所發生的化學沉澱，而後赫胥黎亦坦承錯誤。

Thomas Huxley received the sediments obtained by HMS Cyclops. Under a high power microscope, he found calcareous plates from samples at depths between 3,100 to 4,400 meters. Huxley was the first scientist to recognize coccoliths from marine sediments. However, he attributed an inorganic origin to this discovery, probably because of no coccosphere being recognized then.

In 1868, Huxley re-examined the samples preserved in alcohol. He concluded that the gelatinous mass should be protoplasm, and the calcareous plates scattered within the protoplasm were skeletal elements. Huxley considered the moner to be the simplest form of life, as an evolutionary missing link between living things and non-living ones. He named this new species of *Bathybius haeckelii*. In 1872 the Challenger Expedition began. Ship's scientist noticed that it was a precipitate from seawater that had reacted with the alcohol. Huxley realized that he made a mistake since then.

3

挑戰者號海洋探勘
The Challenger Expedition,
1872-1876

1872 年起，在英國皇家學會的支持之下，湯姆森擔任皇家海軍挑戰者號首席科學家，展開遍及全球的海洋探勘。該航次開創性地以海洋整體為觀察課題進行調查，系統性的水文測量與生物樣本採集，奠定了現代海洋學的基礎，逐步揭露大洋深處不為人知的面貌。

全程歷經三年半的航期，超過十二萬公里的海上航行，共完成 362 測站的觀測作業與標本採集，帶回大量海洋物理與化學的觀測數據，發表超過四千種新物種，奠定了海洋學發展的基礎。在西太平洋關島附近測量到 8,184 公尺的水深，締造了當時已知的最深記錄，此即今日為人熟知的馬里亞納海溝。

The HMS Challenger expedition, sponsored by the British Royal Society, and led by the chief scientist Charles Thomson, began a global ocean investigation and biological collections in 1872. It was the first expedition organized specifically to gather data on a wide range of ocean features, including ocean temperatures seawater chemistry, currents, marine life, and the geology of the seafloor. Thus, the mystery of the deep ocean was gradually revealed.

During the three and a half years cruise, a total number of 362 observation stations were surveyed and a great number of samples were collected in more than 120,000 kilometers of sea voyage. Many discoveries were made to lay the foundation of oceanography in the expedition. The scientific results cataloged over 4,000 previously unknown species. A water depth of 8,184 meters was measured near Guam in the West Pacific as the known deepest place on the ocean floor. As shown by later expeditions, the Challenger Deep was located in the southern end of the Mariana trench.

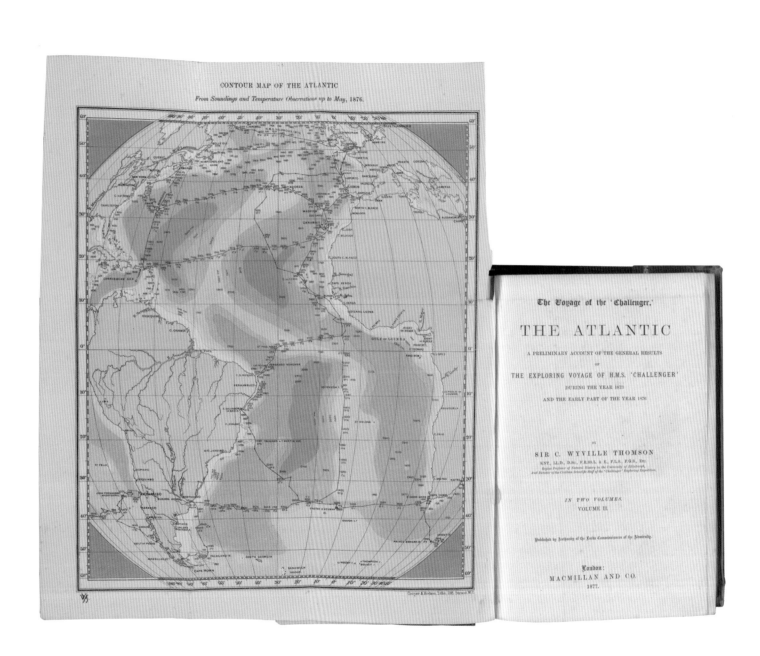

挑戰者號航次於大西洋的科學發現（1877 年出版）

Scientific discoveries by the HMS Challenger in the Atlantic (published in 1877）

Ⓐ 查爾斯・湯姆森（密克羅尼西亞，1997 年）
Charles W. Thomson (Federated States of Micronesia, 1997)

Ⓑ 挑戰者號及測深裝置（崔斯坦，1973 年）
HMS Challenger and the sounding devices
(Tristan da Cunha, 1973)

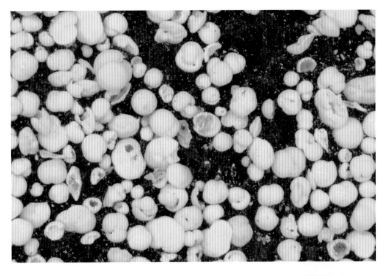

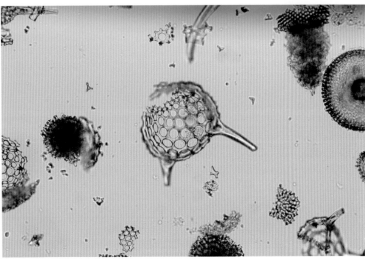

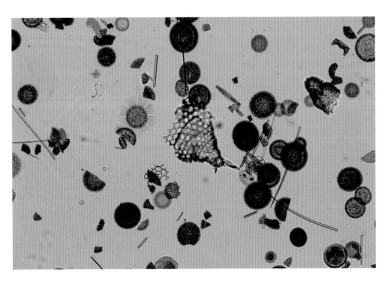

挑戰者號玻片
HMS Challenger slides

Ⓐ 有孔蟲軟泥，採自西北太平洋的 224 站位，水深 3,380 公尺。

Foraminifera ooze, collected from the 224th station in the Pacific Northwest at a water depth of 3,380 meters.

Ⓑ 放射蟲軟泥，採自中部太平洋 266 站位，水深 5,030 公尺。

Radiolaria ooze, collected from the 266th station in Central Pacific at a water depth of 5,030 meters.

Ⓒ 矽藻，採自南大西洋 338 站位，水深 3,700 公尺。

Diatom, collected from the 338th station in South Atlantic at a water depth of 3,700 meters.

挑戰者號顯微玻片
Microscopic Slides from the Challenger Expedition

挑戰者號帶回大量浮游生物拖網與沉積物樣本，微化石成為新奇的研究對象。這些擁有精緻外殼或骨架的迷人生物，主要為棲息於海洋表層的放射蟲、有孔蟲、矽藻，以其種類繁多、型態殊異，令人驚艷於此一彷若繁星的小宇宙。

科學家自此掌握全球海底沉積物的分布特性，發現大洋底部普遍分布保存有孔蟲殼體的鈣質軟泥，但超過一定深度之後，青白的沉積物轉而以紅黏土為主，原先散佈其中的有孔蟲殼體，或是破損、或是消失，取而代之的是放射蟲、矽藻成為沉積物之主要構成。

The HMS Challenger brought back a large amount of plankton tow and sediment samples. Since then, microfossils became a novel research subject. The microscopic organisms, with exquisite shells and skeletons, are mainly radiolaria, foraminifera and diatoms which have been living in the surface ocean. With a wide variety of species and forms, one may be truly amazed at this tiny microcosm.

Since scientists had known the characteristic distributions of the marine sediments, it was realized that the calcareous ooze, covering lots of the world ocean's floor, was mainly composed of the calcareous shells of the foraminifera. Beyond certain depths, the pale-white sediments turned to red clay mainly composing of siliceous radiolaria and diatom shells with severe dissolution of calcareous foraminiferal shells in the deepest area.

Ⓓ 有孔蟲與翼足類，採自澳洲東北部的 185 站位，水深 290 公尺。

Foraminifera and pteropods, collected from the 185th station in north-east Australia at a water depth of 290 meters.

Ⓔ 有孔蟲為主的生物碎屑，採自西南太平洋的 298 站位，水深 4,180 公尺。

Foraminifera-based biological debris, collected from the 298th station in the south-west Pacific at a water depth of 4,180 meters.

微化石的藝術與科學 Art and Science of Microfossil

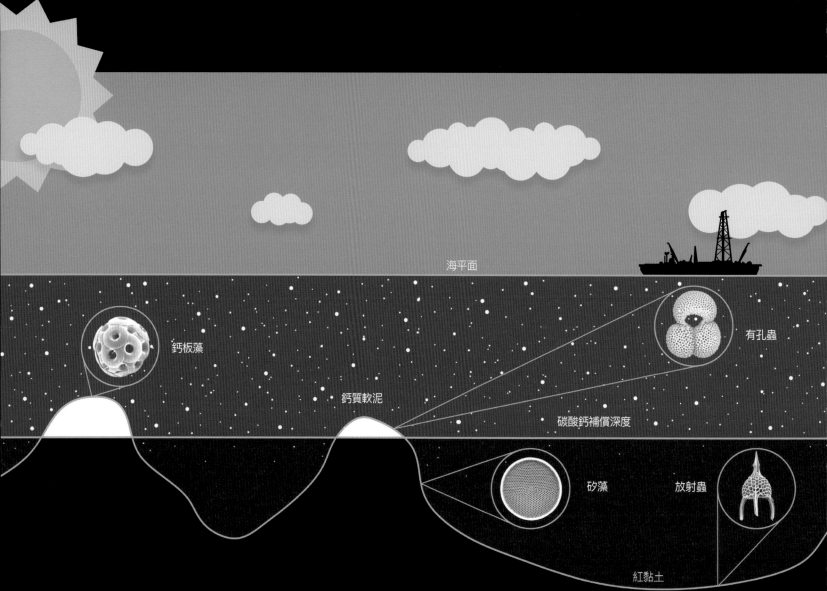

海平面

鈣板藻

有孔蟲

鈣質軟泥

碳酸鈣補償深度

矽藻

放射蟲

紅黏土

深海雪線
Marine Snow Line in the Deep

海洋浮游生物死後沉降到幽冥深處，一片片不斷飄落的深海雪花，猶如一場持續數億年之久的無盡雪季。如果將海水抽離，海床上理當佈滿各式微體化石，卻只見水深較淺的海底山頭鋪蓋白色鈣質軟泥，這道猶如陸地上高山雪線的界面，稱之為碳酸鈣補償深度。

這是因為有孔蟲、鈣板藻殼體保存狀態與不同深度的底層水質有關。當生物殼體沉降至水深二、三千公尺附近的海床，碳酸鈣開始遭受明顯的溶蝕作用；而在碳酸鈣補償深度之下，碳酸鈣幾乎溶蝕殆盡，沉積物只剩下黏土，因顏色偏紅褐色，稱為紅黏土。挑戰者號當年橫越大西洋採集不同深度的海底沉積物，就已發現這個現象。

In the deep ocean, marine snow is a continuous shower of organic materials from above, flake upon flake, layer upon layer – a drift that has lasted for hundreds of millions of years. The settling of calbonate shells does not universally blanket the ocean floor. This type of calcareous ooze accumulates only above the carbonate compensation depth (CCD). The link of the ooze boundary to elevation has invited comparison to the snow line on land.

The preservation of foraminifera and coccolithophore is controlled by the property of the bottom waters at different depths. As depth and pressure increases within the water column, the corresponding carbonate saturation state decreases and the shells start to dissolve. Below the CCD, the rate of supply lags behide the rate of dissolution, such that no calcareous microfossil is preserved. The red clays are red to chocolate brown in color, and enriched siliceous microfossils. The depth-dependent characteristic of seafloor sediments was first discovered during the HMS Challenger trans-Atlantic cruise.

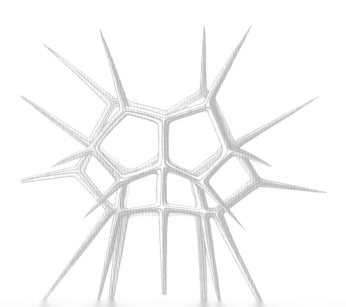

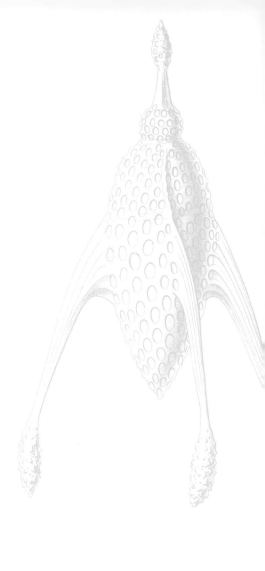

Ⓐ Ⓑ 挑戰者號報告之放射蟲（塞內加爾，1973 年）
Radiolaria draw from the Challenger's report (Senegal, 1973)

Ⓒ Ⓓ 挑戰者號報告之放射蟲（塞內加爾，1972 年）
Radiolaria draw from the Challenger's report (Senegal, 1972)

挑戰者號成果報告
Scientific Reports from the Challenger Expedition

挑戰者號帶回為數可觀的觀測數據及珍貴樣本，委由歐美各國最負盛名的學者進行研究，全面性地修訂海洋生物各重要類別的分類架構。歷經三年半的航期，所完成首度全球不同深度的水溫資料普查，成為百年後評估海洋暖化最重要的參考依據。

英國布雷迪擔任有孔蟲的研究，其成果報告於 1884 年出版，恢弘詳實的分類以及精美的圖板，至今仍是進行有孔蟲分類必不可缺的工具書。海克爾負責放射蟲的分類與鑑定，顯微鏡下辛勤工作的總結，新種發表竟達三千五百種之多，完成一百四十幅圖版，成果報告於 1887 年正式出版。

After the HMS Challenger expedition, the accumulation of measured hydrographic data and valuable biological samples was unprecedented. The shore-based studies were carrying out by the most distinguished scholars. As a result, a comprehensive revision of the classification of marine life had been made. After three and a half years' investigation, the first global survey of water temperature profiles was completed. The collected hydrographic data became the most prestigious reference for evaluating ocean warming over the last one hundred years.

Henry Brady conducted foraminiferal research and the monograph was published in 1884. With extensive and detailed classification and exquisite plates, the book remains one of the most frequently cited reference on this group. In the meantime, Ernst Haeckel was responsible for the radiolarian. Working diligently under the microscope, he described as many as 3,500 new species with illustrations of one hundred and forty plates. Haeckel's results were officially published in 1887.

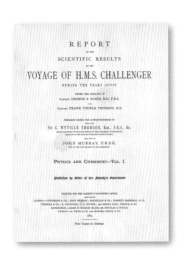

挑戰者號水文調查報告（1884 年出版）
The HMS Challenger report on hydrological investigation (published in 1884)

微化石的藝術與科學 Art and Science of Microfossil

自然界的藝術形態
Nature's Art Forms

德國生物學家海克爾畢生致力於探尋生物型態的極致美感，具體呈現此一理念的《自然界的藝術形態》於 1904 年結集出書，全書以一百幅版畫來詮釋海克爾的演化觀點，簡單生命形態與時俱進地漸趨繁複，而複雜生命則追求形態的至善完美。對當代科學和藝術均產生深遠影響。

透過顯微鏡觀察，單細胞生物最能傳達造物幾何結構之美，只見放射蟲精緻結構的骨架巧奪天工，矽藻晶瑩剔透的殼蓋脫俗典雅，有孔蟲造型多變的殼體風格獨具，海克爾的細膩筆觸對於掌握型態細節格外出色，確能傳達生物型態完美對稱的理念。

恩斯特 · 海克爾（1834-1919）
Ernst Haeckel (1834-1919)

The German biologist Ernst Haeckel devoted himself to pursue the ultimate aesthetics of the biological forms. His book, entitled *Art Forms in Nature*, faithfully illustrated the idea of symmetry and level organization. The book used one hundred plates of lithograph prints, collectively published in 1904, to outline his philosophy on evolution. The natural life evolved progressively from simple to complexity, and from complexity to perfect symmetry. Haeckel's illustration had a profound influence on the contemporary science and art.

Through the microscope, single-cell organisms could best demonstrate the perfect geometry and symmetry. The delicate structure of radiolaria showed exquisite craftsmanship; the crystal shell of the diatomite was refined; and the shell style of the foraminifera was unique. Haeckel's images on these microfossils were extraordinary to convey the idea that "simple is more".

Thalamophora. — Kammerlinge.

有孔蟲（石版印刷，1904 年出版）

Foraminifera (Lithography print; published in 1904)

微化石的藝術與科學　Art and Science of Microfossil

Thalamophora. — Kammerlinge.

有孔蟲（石版印刷，
1904 年出版）
Foraminifera
(Lithography print;
published in 1904)

Diatomea. — Schachtellinge.

矽藻（石版印刷，1904
年出版）

Diatom (Lithography
print; published in 1904)

Cyrtoidea. — Flaſchenſtrahlinge.

微化石的藝術與科學　Art and Science of Microfossil

放射蟲（石版印刷，
1904 年出版）

Radiolaria (Lithography
print; published in 1904)

Spumellaria. — Schaumstrahlinge.

放射蟲（石版印刷，
1904 年出版）

Radiolaria (Lithography
print; published in 1904)

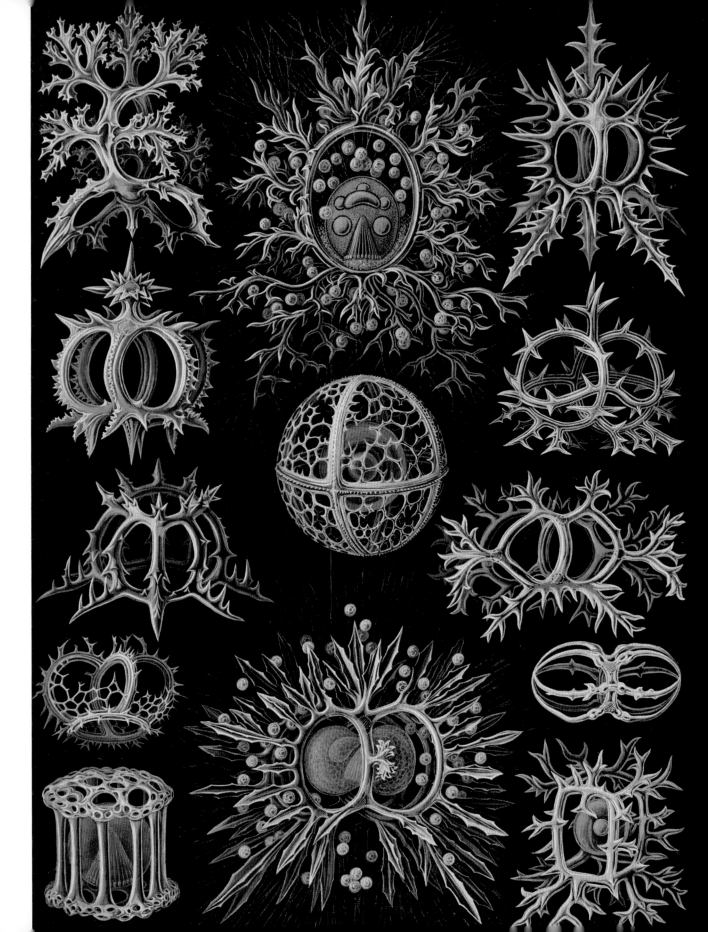

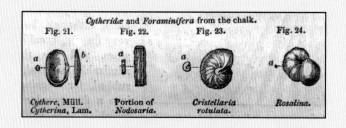

清代地學古籍
Geology Books of the Qing Dynasty

十九世紀下半葉，來華的傳教士引入了西方近代科學。這批最早期譯成中文的地學書籍，包括《地學淺釋》、《地學指略》、《地學須知》、《地學啟蒙》等，對於不久前才佈設於北大西洋的海底電纜，白堊岩層的生物成因，有孔蟲於環境和年代上的應用，都有篇幅介紹。

但從字裡行間閱讀這些翻譯文字卻顯得生硬，特別是人名、地名或學名因採用音譯，讀來格外詰屈聱牙，遇到一長串音節如咒語般的拉丁學名，這挑戰就更為艱澀。

In the second half of the 19th century, modern sciences were introduced to China by the Western missionaries. The earlier translated Chinese books included *Elements of Geology, Guide to Geology, Geology Notes* and *Geology Primer*. Some of the updated information on microfossils was mentioned, for examples, the trans-Atlantic underwater cable, the biogenous origin of chalk formation, and the environmental and chronologic applications of foraminifera.

However, reading these translated texts between the lines was no easy task. It was because the scientific terminology and technical vocabulary were yet established in China. Once encounter the scientific name of microfossils, the translator usually adopted a loanword instead of a paraphrase. Accordingly, a translated Chinese name always sounds like a long string syllables of Latin mantra.

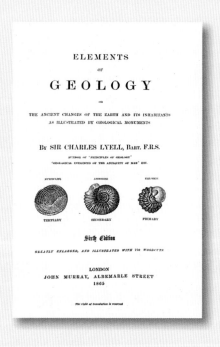

《地質學綱要》
英國萊爾著，第六版，1865 年出版
Elements of Geology
by Charles Lyell, 6th edition, 1865.

《地學淺釋》
Elements of Geology

《地學淺釋》是最早以中文出版的地質學專門著作，1871 年由
江南製造局所設翻譯館刊行。該書由瑪高溫與華蘅芳合力完成翻
譯，原本出自英國萊爾 (雷俠兒) 所著《地質學綱要》第六版 (1865
年出版)。原書附有超過兩百幅精美刻製的插圖，經翻刻成木刻
版畫，另有一番風味。

The *Elements of Geology* was the earliest published geology book
in Chinese, published in 1871 by the translation department of
the Jiangnan Arsenal. The translation was carried out by Daniel
Jerome Magowan and Hua Hengfang. The Chinese version was
based on the 6th edition of the *Elements of Geology* by Charles
Lyell published in 1865.

Ⓐ

Ⓐ 以茶而刻粉置水中，不過一細粒，若以顯微鏡視
　之，其細粒皆是殭石，形甚分明，每一斤茶而刻
　中，有殭石千餘，其中有四種最多。

Ⓑ《地學淺釋》（1896 年，石印本）
　（英）雷俠爾著，（美）瑪高溫口譯，華蘅芳筆述
Elements of Geology
by Charles Lyell, Chinese translation by D. J.
Magowan and Hua Hengfang.

Ⓑ

《地學指略》
Guide to Geology

《地學指略》於 1881 年由上海益智書會出版，由英國來華傳教士文教治口譯，李慶軒筆述，前者擔負口頭翻譯將英文轉化為華語，再由後者潤飾摘錄的文字後，轉化成中文篇章，全書分三卷十九章。

The *Guide to Geology* was published in 1881 by the Shanghai School and Textbook Series Committee. The English-Chinese translation processes were first conducted by oral translation by British missionary George Sydney Owen. And then the recorded manuscript was rephrased by Li Qingxuan. The *Guide to Geology* was divided into three volumes with a total of 19 chapters.

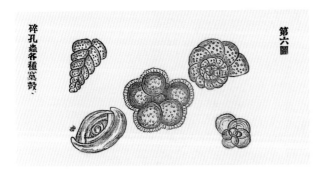

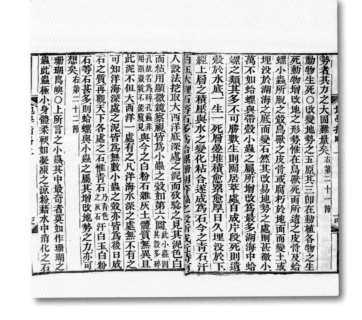

《地學指略》（1881 年，初刻本）

（英）文教治口譯，李慶軒筆述

Guide to Geology

Chinese translation by G. S. Owen and Li Qingxuan.

《地學啟蒙》
Geology Primer

《地學啟蒙》於 1886 年由上海總稅務司署出版，由英國傳教士、漢學家艾約瑟翻譯。他受聘於中國海關期間致力於將西方科學轉譯中文，完成了《西學啟蒙十六種》，涵蓋了動物學、植物學、地質學、化學、邏輯學等領域。《地學啟蒙》全書八卷，論述水中淤積之層疊石、動植物所遺體殼質積成之層疊石等。

The *Geology Prime* was published by the Inspectorate General at Shanghai in 1886. It was edited and translated by the British missionary, sinologist Joseph Edkins. He was appointed by the Customs to edit and translate a series of western scientific works into Chinese, and the fruits were the *16 Primers for Western Knowledge*, including zoology, botany, geology, chemistry, logic and other subjects. The *Geology Primer* consisted of eight volumes, describing the sedimentary rock and the biological sedimentary rock originated from the fossil remains of animals and plants.

《地學啟蒙》（1898 年·石印本）
（英）蓋凱著，（英）艾約瑟譯
Geology Primer
by Archibald Geike, Chinese translation by Joseph Edkins

THE TAIWAN MUSEUM

NO.   DATE

Lepidocyclina verbeeki

FAM.   台北縣山子腳

LOC   IDENT. BY   何新也

中新世

Lepidocyclina verbeeki

有孔虫化石

臺灣總督府博物館所藏品

臺灣省立博

編 號 F01-08

品 名 Lepidocyclina

有孔虫化石

地質系統 中新世

產 地 台北縣 山子腳

採集者

臺灣省立博物館

名 有孔蟲化石

名 Lepidocyclina verbeeki

地 台北縣 山子腳

集年月   編號 F01-08   № 138

記 Miocene 中新世

品

學

科

產

採集年

附

THE TAIWAN MUS

NO.   DATE

Lepidocyclina verbeeki

FAM.   台北縣山子腳

LOC   IDENT. BY

臺灣省立博物館

編 號 F01-08   NO.138

品 名 Lepidocyclina verbeeki

有孔虫化石

地質系統 中新世

產 地 台北縣 山子腳

採集者   日期

Lepidocyclina verbeeki （Newton & Holland, 1899）

產地：山子腳‧新北市｜年代：中新世（臺灣總督府博物館入藏）

Lepidocyclina verbeeki (Newton & Holland, 1899)

Location: Shantzjiao, New Taipei City ｜ Age: Miocene (Collection of the Museum of the Government of Taiwan)

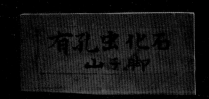

有孔虫化石
山子腳

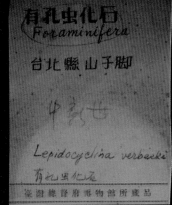

有孔虫化石
Foraminifera

台北縣 山子腳

中新世

Lepidocyclina verbeeki

有孔虫化石

臺灣總督府博物館所藏品

品

品

地質系

產

採集年

3

臺灣的微化石
Microfossil Studies in
Taiwan

" 海底沉積物是地球的史詩。如果人類夠聰明，或許就能從中讀取地球歷史。

The sediments are a sort of epic poem of the earth. When we are wise enough, perhaps we can read in them all of past history "

—— 瑞秋・卡森（*Rachel Carson, 1907 - 1964*）

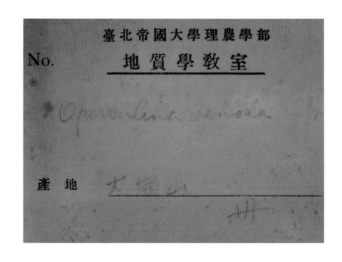

Operculina venosa〔Fichtel & Moll, 1798〕
產地：大岡山，高雄市｜年代：全新世（原臺北帝國大學所藏）

Operculina venosa (Fichtel & Moll, 1798)

Location: Dagangshan, Kaohsiung ｜ Age: Holocene
(Transfer from the Taihoku Imperial University)

臺灣微化石研究始自日治時期的地質調查工作。1899年小藤文次郎與德永重康採集北臺灣地層所產化石，送交英國學者Newton和Holland研究，於1900年發表石灰岩中顯微玻片之化石鑑定，辨識出有孔蟲屬種包括 *Lepidocyclina verbeeki, Gypsina, Miliolina, Pulvinulina, Globigerina* 等，為臺灣微化石研究最早見諸文獻者。

隨著日治時期地質調查工作逐步遍及全臺，大型有孔蟲以其較易於保存鑑定特徵，成為主要研究對象，對於地層年代的判定提供重要依據。1945年之後，中央地質調查所與中油探採研究所相繼成立，小型有孔蟲和鈣質超微化石的運用陸續展開，臺灣島的前世與今生有了更多的了解。

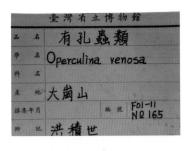

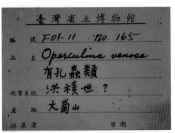

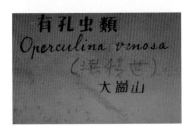

The microfossil studies in Taiwan began with the geological surveys during the Japanese rule period. In 1899, Bunjiro Koto and Shigeyasu Tokunaga collected fossils from the North Taiwan and sent them to the British scholars Bullen Newton and Richard Holland for research. In 1900, they published fossil content in limestone slides by microscopic examination, identifying foraminifera species including *Lepidocyclina verbeeki, Gypsina, Miliolina, Pulvinulina, Globigerina*, etc. This was the earliest report on Taiwan microfossils documented in the literature.

Geological investigation had gradually been extended to the whole island since then. The large foraminifera were the major dating tools as they were relatively easy to preserve and determine, and could provide important base to determine the age of the rock formations. After 1945, the Central Geological Survey and Petroleum Exploration and Research Institute were established. The applications of small foraminifera and calcareous nannofossils were developed and carried out subsequently. It has since got a deeper insight of the geological past of Taiwan Island.

苗栗出礦坑地質圖（1930 年出版）
Geological Map of the Chuhuangkeng area in Miaoli (published in 1930)

出礦坑油氣田
The Chuhuangkeng Oilfield

臺灣雖位居清國邊陲，出礦坑卻擁有第一座以機器開鑿的油井。早在 1860 年代，客家先民於苗栗公館後龍溪畔發現浮油，以人工挖掘深約一丈的淺井，汲取後販售作燈油之用。1878 年，清政府招募美國技師簡時和絡克來臺鑽井，但僅鑽獲少量油氣未能正式量產。

日治時期引進現代化的地質探勘技術及開採設備，推斷出礦坑背斜擁有良好的儲油氣構造，便在此約略呈南北向的背斜軸部開鑿油井，先後鑽取了近百口之數，經多年開採，淺層油氣井逐漸枯竭。二戰之後，台灣中油公司在苗栗設立臺灣油礦探勘處，積極展開全臺儲油氣構造評估，出礦坑因深鑽而再度獲致大量油氣。

Although Taiwan was situated on the marginal territory of the Qing Empire, it possessed the first mechanically drilled oil well in China. As early as the 1860s, Hakka ancestors had found oil slicks on the banks of the Houlong Creek in Gongguan, Miaoli. They manually dug a shallow hole to collect oil for sale as lamp oil. In 1878, the Qing government recruited two American technicians, A. Port Karns and Robert D. Locke, to Taiwan. They succeeded only in extract a small amount of oil, but not good enough for mass production.

Since the rule of Taiwan, Japanese introduced modern geological exploration technology and mining equipment. They found that the Chuhuangkeng anticline was a structural trap in which oil and gas accumulated, and started to drill many sites along the north-south anticline axis. For many years, nearly one hundred wells had been drilled, and the production declined steadily in the shallow layers. After World War II, the CPC set up the Oilfield Exploration Office in Miaoli to carry out re-evaluation of oil reservoirs all over the island. Once again, deep drilling wells brought Chuhuangkeng back to a vigorous production of oil and natural gas.

Ⓐ 紡錘蟲化石
產地 : 美濃，日本 | 年代 : 石炭紀
Parafusulina Japonica (Gümbel, 1874)
Location: Mino, Japan | Age: Carboniferous

Ⓑ 紡錘蟲化石
堪薩斯州 , 美國 | 年代 : 晚石炭紀
Fusulinid Fossil
Location: Kansas, USA | Age: Late Carboniferous

Ⓐ

Ⓑ

2

臺灣最古老的化石
The Oldest Fossils in
Taiwan Island

臺灣地質調查研究開展於日治時期，由於中央山脈的東斜面主要為大南澳變質岩區，經過多次變質作用，大部分化石都遭受破壞。日治時期所發現的化石，年代較老的均來自中央山脈西斜面的板岩和硬頁岩帶，這些大型有孔蟲包括 *Discocyclina*（盤原蟲）、*Nummulites*（貨幣蟲）和 *Assilina*（阿西蟲），年代可以回推到新生代早期的始新世，距今約五千萬年前。

臺灣地區已知最古老的化石，是 1951 年顏滄波在臺灣東部大南澳變質岩區的發現，經鑑定為二疊紀的䗴目有孔蟲（紡錘蟲）和珊瑚化石，填補了過去日人僅發現新生代化石之缺憾。這些生存於古生代具有年代指示意義的紡錘蟲化石，年代距今約三億多年前至兩億五千萬年前，提供放射性元素定年的方法之外，關鍵的古生物實體證據。

The Geological survey of Taiwan began since the Japanese rule period. The Tananao Metamorphic Complex distributes mainly in the eastern flank of the Central Mountain Range. Most of the fossils had already been destroyed by numerous metamorphic activities, and the age of the Complex could hardly be determined by the fossil content. During the Japanese period, the relatively older fossils all came from the slate and argillite in the western flank of the Central Mountain Range. The large foraminifera found including *Discocyclina*, *Nummulites* and *Assilina*, indicating an age of Eocene in Early Cenozoic, about 50 million years ago.

The oldest fossils known in Taiwan were discovered by Tsang-Po Yen in the Tananao metamorphic rock area in eastern Taiwan in 1951. They were identified as Permian fusulinid foraminifera and corals, dating back to between 250 and 300 million years ago. Thus, the shortcoming that only Cenozoic fossils were reported previously by the Japanese was eliminated. Fusulina, an excellent index fossil for the Permian rocks, could provide an alternative method for radioactive dating.

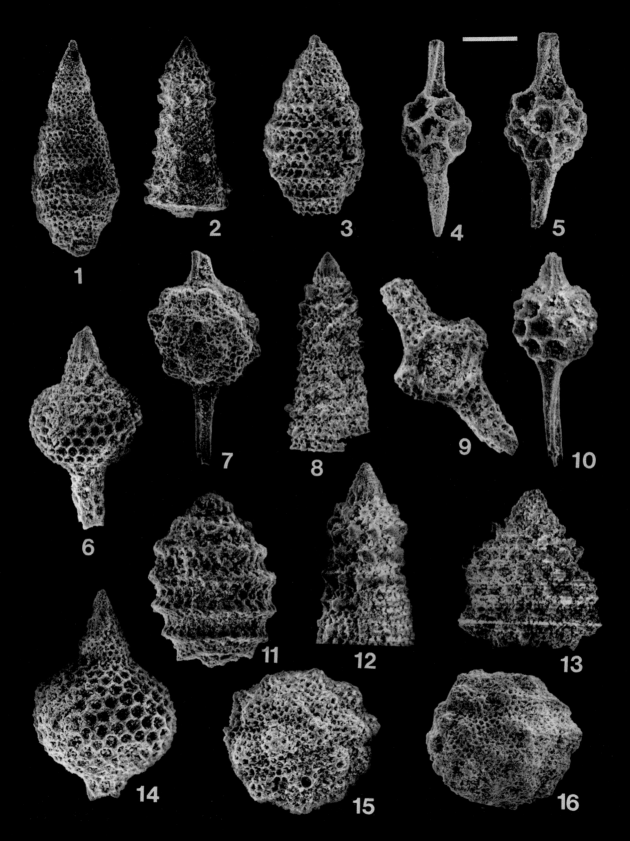

3

蘭嶼白堊紀放射蟲
Cretaceous Radiolaria from the Orchid Island

位於臺灣東南的蘭嶼是晚新生代火山活動的產物，近年在島上發現含有放射蟲的紅色矽質岩，原屬於深海盆地典型的大洋沉積物，形成於超過碳酸鈣補償深度的深海環境。經過化石鑑定和分析結果，蘭嶼放射蟲族群的年代屬於白堊紀早期。

Orchid Island, located off the southeastern coast of Taiwan, was a product of Late Cenozoic volcanic activity. In recent years, radiolarians have been discovered in red chert samples, the typical pelagic sediments in ocean basin below the Carbonate Compensation Depth. The results of fossil identification and analysis indicated that the age of the radiolarian assemblage was Early Cretaceous.

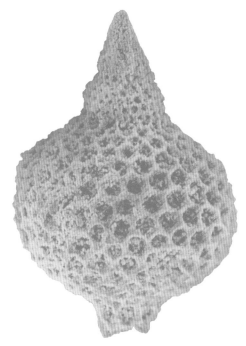

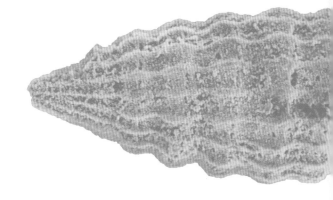

蘭嶼早白堊紀放射蟲化石圖版
Plate of Early Cretaceous radiolaria fossils from the Orchid Island

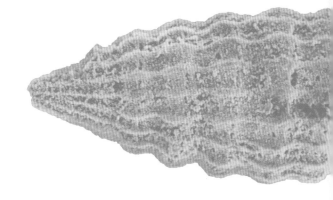

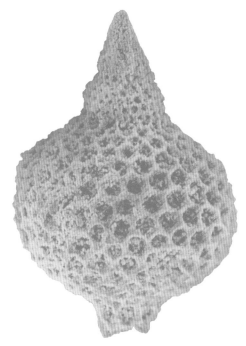

臺灣的微化石　Microfossil Studies in Taiwan

滄海桑田的臺灣海峽
Emerged Land Bridge from the Taiwan Strait

臺灣西南平原與臺灣海峽接壤相鄰，地表下的地層深受海平面升降影響至鉅，不僅沉積物顆粒大小有所差異，地層中的化石組成也相應而變。中央地質調查所為評估曾文溪流域地下水資源，曾於此鑽取岩心以探查地下地層三維分布格局，由岩心中發現有孔蟲的層位，揭露臺灣海峽曾多次經歷滄海桑田。

每當冰河時期到臨，全球海水面下降幅度可達一百公尺，導致臺灣海峽出露成為陸地，大型哺乳動物可在此倘佯生活，死亡後的骨骸就在原地埋藏。如今漁民在澎湖水道撈取的化石，包括象齒、鹿角、各類哺乳動物獸骨，就是明證。

Taiwan's south-western plain lies next to the Taiwan Strait. The subsurface strata have been greatly influenced by sea level rises and falls. Variation occurs not only in the grain size of sediment but also in the fossil composition. To assess the groundwater resources of the Zeng Wen River Basin, several cores were drilled by the Central Geological Survey to explore the three-dimensional distribution of underground formations. Foraminifera were found in some intervals of the cores, and revealed that the Taiwan Strait had undergone dramatic sea level changes.

The amplitude of sea level drop was over 100 meter during glacial time, which results in the emergence of the present-day seafloor in the Taiwan Strait. Large terrestrial mammal should wonder and flourish around the land bridge between Taiwan and Mainland China. This implication is support by those fossil fauna collected by the fish man in the Penghu Channel, such as elephant teeth, dear antler, and other different kinds of mammal bones.

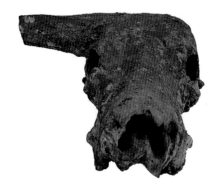

德氏水牛
Bubalus teilhardi Young 1932

如何採集海洋微化石？

How to Collect Marine Microfossil?

微化石難以用肉眼辨識，必須將埋藏它的沉積物一起採集。沉積物樣品可採取自陸上地層出露的沉積岩、地下鑽井所取得岩心、或是海洋底部的鬆散沉積物，經過適當處理，再用不同方法予以分離，方能獲得所需的微化石。海洋沉積物樣本主要採集方式有二：以海底表面為中心挖取四周底質的抓泥器，和將管柱插入底質採集柱狀沉積物的岩心採樣器。

Microfossils are hard to be identified with the naked eye, so they should be collected together with the sediments. Field samples may come from the surface outcrops, drilling cores, and loose sediments in the seabed. They need to be properly treated to obtain fossil specimens for further studies. There are two major approaches to collect the marine sediments. One is to use a clamshell bucket to grab the sediments around; and the other is to penetrate a long tube into the bottom to obtain sediment cores.

Ⓐ

Ⓑ

Ⓐ 活塞岩心採樣
Calypso giant piston coring

Ⓑ 箱型岩心採樣
Giant box core sampling

海上岩心採樣作業
Core sampling operation in the sea

微體古生物學家的研究室

Micropaleontologist's Laboratory

有孔蟲和放射蟲化石由於個體較大，可透過立體顯微鏡進行挑揀。將前處理過的樣本散佈於視野寬廣黑底白線的觀察皿上，進行逐格觀察，一但發現微化石，即用濕潤的細毛筆將化石輕輕黏起，移置微體玻片之上，再用稀釋的膠水使之固定，闔上活動蓋玻片，以供鑑定。一位專業的微體古生物學家需隨時掌握完備的化石圖鑑，才能正確的對於微化石進行鑑定。

Foraminiferal and radiolarian fossils are relatively large in size, so they can be picked up under stereo microscope. The prepared samples spread over an observation plate with a wide field of view. Detailed inspection is proceeded grid-by-grid. Once the target microfossil is spotted, it can be gently picked up by a fine paint brush, dipping its tip with water. The chosen specimen is then relocated to a microscopic slide, and fixed by diluted glue. The slide is then covered up, and the specimen is ready for identification. A professional micropaleontologist needs to acquire extensive knowledge of the illustrated handbook and publications in order to correctly identify microfossils.

星砂 : 見證大海的浪漫

Star Sand: The Romance of the Sea

具有星芒狀突出外型的星砂，生活在陽光普照的淺海珊瑚礁，死後殼體被海浪沖打到沙灘，成為造訪海邊不經意的驚奇發現。仔細端詳這些砂粒般大小的有孔蟲殼體，還可以細分為好幾個造型互異的種，同屬於底棲性有孔蟲。

Star sands are distinct in their morphology of star shaped shells. When they die, their shells remain in the shallow coral reef and the tide brings them ashore. This results in beaches sprinkled with star sand. Under the microscope, you may identifiy morphology of various designs from different benthic foraminiferal species.

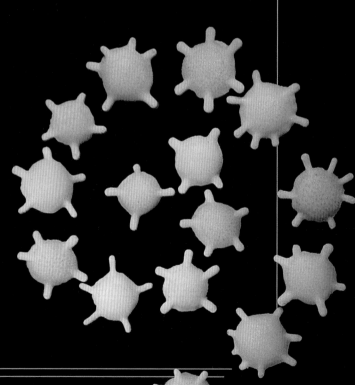

來自海底的浮游有孔蟲

Planktonic Foraminifera from the Bottom of the Sea

廣佈於全球各大洋的浮游性有孔蟲，居無定所地漂浮於海洋透光帶，死後殼體沉降至海床。圓鼓鼓的外型是其共同特徵，深海沉積物由於長時間累積由上方送來的浮游性有孔蟲，種類雖然不多，數量往往要比底棲性有孔蟲來得多。

Planktonic foraminifera are widespread over the upper waters of global oceans. Most of them live in the photic zone and sink to th bottom as they die. The common features are the globular chambers that provide buoyancy. As the accumulation of the settling shells continuing over a long time, planktonic foraminifera are the dominant constitutions in the pelagic sediments, while benthic foraminifera are rare to be found.

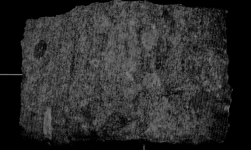

大型有孔蟲也是微化石？

Are Larger Foraminifera Considered to be Microfossil?

有孔蟲個體通常在數百微米至數公厘之間，然而貨幣石之類的大型有孔蟲居然可達到數公分之多。原因在於大型有孔蟲鑑定屬種之時，必須先將化石磨製成顯微玻片，在顯微鏡下觀察初始房室及後續房室如何增生與排列，因此仍被視為微化石研究對象。

The typical size of foraminifer range between 0.1mm to 1mm, but larger foraminifer may reach up to 100 mm or more. Studies of foraminifera in thin-section have chiefly been applied to the larger foraminifera. Identification to the species level oftern requires a detailed examination of internal structures under the microscope. This is why they are considered to be a microfossil research subject as well.

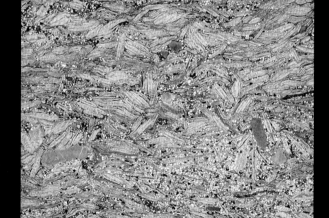

Operculina sp. （口蓋蟲屬）
地點：南投國姓（桂竹林層） | 年代：中新世
Operculina sp.
Location: Guoshing, Nantou | Age: Miocene

Ⓐ

Ⓑ

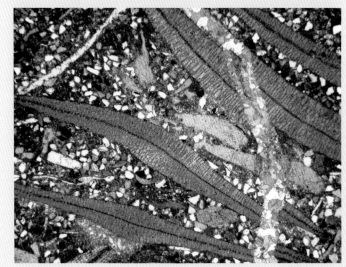

Ⓐ *Operculina* sp.（口蓋蟲屬）
　　地點：南投國姓（石門層）｜年代：中新世
　　Operculina sp.
　　Location: Guoshing, Nantou ｜ Age: Miocene

Ⓑ *Discocyclina* sp.（圓旋蟲屬）
　　地點：南投中寮｜年代：始新世
　　Discocyclina sp.
　　Location: Jungliau, Nantou ｜ Age: Eocene

鈣板藻：偏光顯微鏡下的燦爛星空
Coccolithophore: Bright Stars under Polarized Light Microscope

用來觀察鈣板藻的主要工具為偏光顯微鏡，和常見的解剖顯微鏡不同處，在於物鏡上、下方各別插入了偏光片，使光線只能以特定的振盪方向穿透化石玻片。因鈣板主要是由各式方解石晶體構成，在偏光顯微鏡下會呈現出高亮白色的影像，而玻片透過戴物臺以不同角度旋轉，其影像會隨之產生改變，形態和特徵也更加明顯，最適合用來快速鑑定鈣質超微化石的屬種。

The main tool for observing coccolithophore is polarized light microscope rather than optical stereo microscope. The main difference is added polarizing plates, to the upper and the lower of the objective lens, to convert natural light into polarized light. Directly transmitted light through samples can be blocked with a polarizer orientated at 90 degrees to the illumination. As coccoliths are composed of different oriented calcite crystals, they show a highest bright white image under polarized microscope. Many morphology features of calcareous nannofossils will allow identification down to species level.

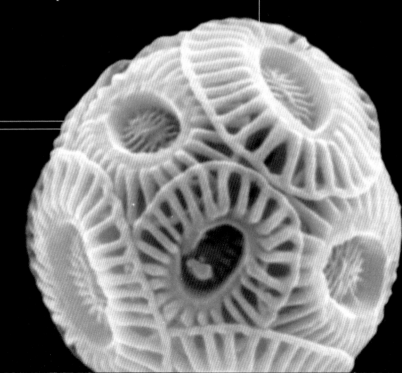

電子顯微鏡下的赫氏艾密里藻
Emiliania huxleyi under scanning electron microscope

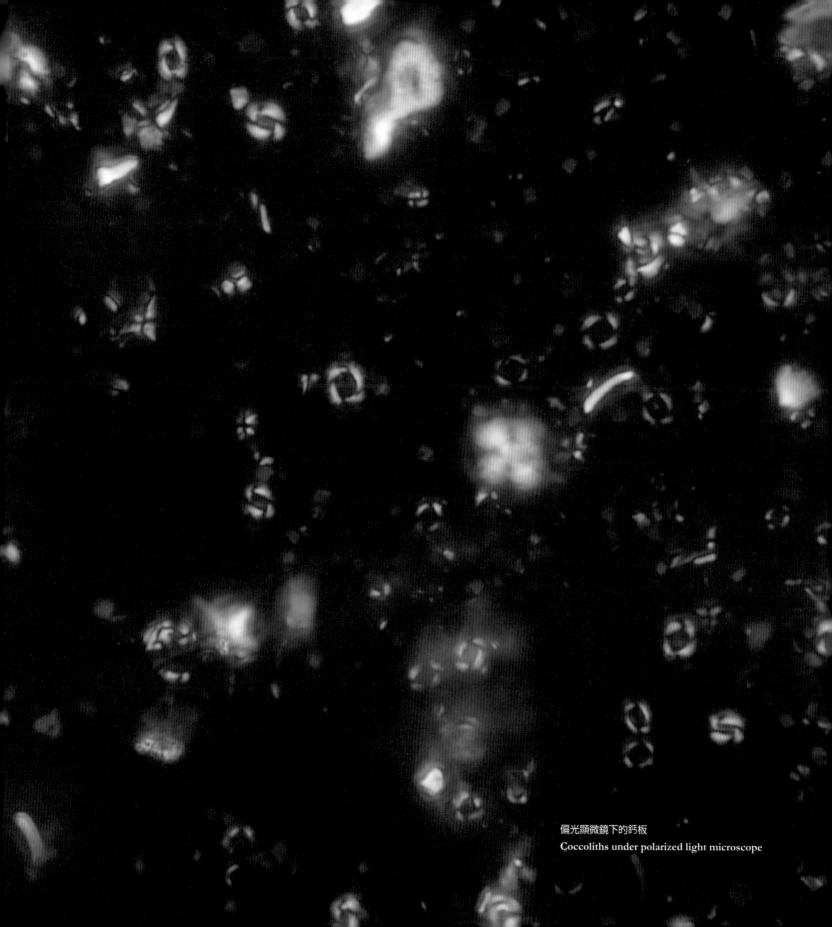

偏光顯微鏡下的鈣板
Coccoliths under polarized light microscope

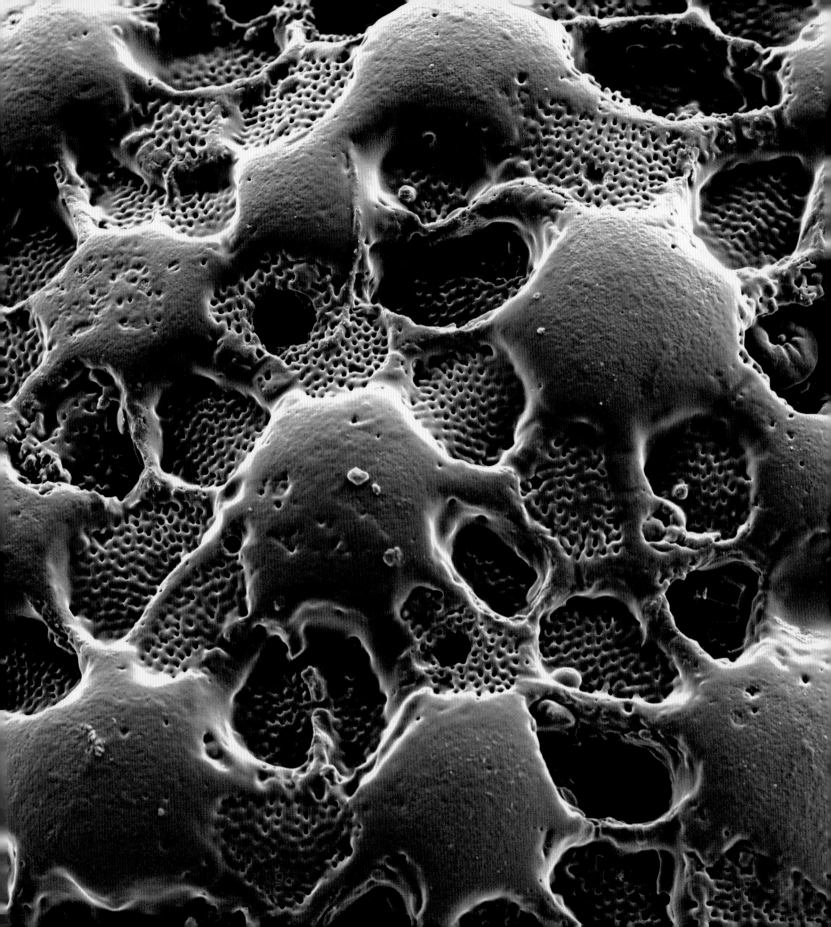

4

見微知著探未來
Seeing the Future in a
Grain of Microfossil

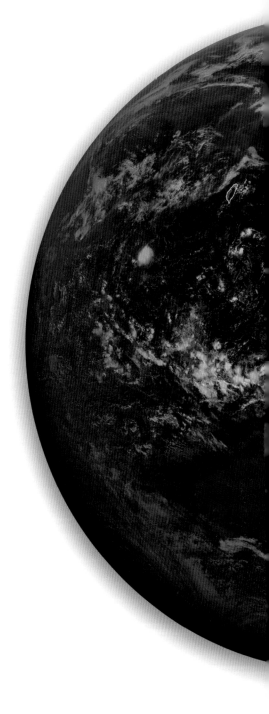

"

地質成因費時千年所造成的氣候變遷。如今我們將在一生之中
經歷，而且將是逐年的快速惡化。

*Geological change usually takes thousands of years to happen but we
are seeing the climate changing not just in our lifetimes but also year
by year.*

"

—— 洛夫洛克（*James Lovelock, 1919-* ）

矽藻及鈣板藻是海洋食物金字塔的基礎生產者，對於調節地球氣候扮演重要角色，有如維持地球溫度恆定的空調器。反觀人類種種破壞生態環境的作為，衍生出各類海洋文明病，如海洋酸化將使得建造碳酸鈣殼體的有孔蟲、鈣板藻面臨骨質酥鬆症般的生存危機，而遍布各大洋的塑膠微粒持續累積增加，已經成為浮游國度難以驅除的不速之客。在全球人口即將突破八十億的當下，人類應該以地球系統的巨觀角度來思考生命與環境之間應如何永續共榮。

Diatoms and coccolithophores are two major primary producers of the trophic pyramid in marine ecology. They play an important role in regulating the global climate system, working like a thermostat to maintain the stability of Earth's temperature. In contrast, the environmental disturbance by human activity has generated all kinds of marine civilization diseases. For example, ocean acidification makes organisms such as foraminifera and coccolithophore more difficulty for calcification to build carbonate shells. The continuing accumulation of the microplastics is widespread over the ocean, and the ubiquitous invader is laborious to clear away from the Plankton World. On the eve of the global population breaking through the 8 billion mark, everyone should reassess human interference with life and environment under a macroscopic view of the earth system.

Himawari 8 衛星從太空看地球

Seeing earth from space by Himawari 8 satellite

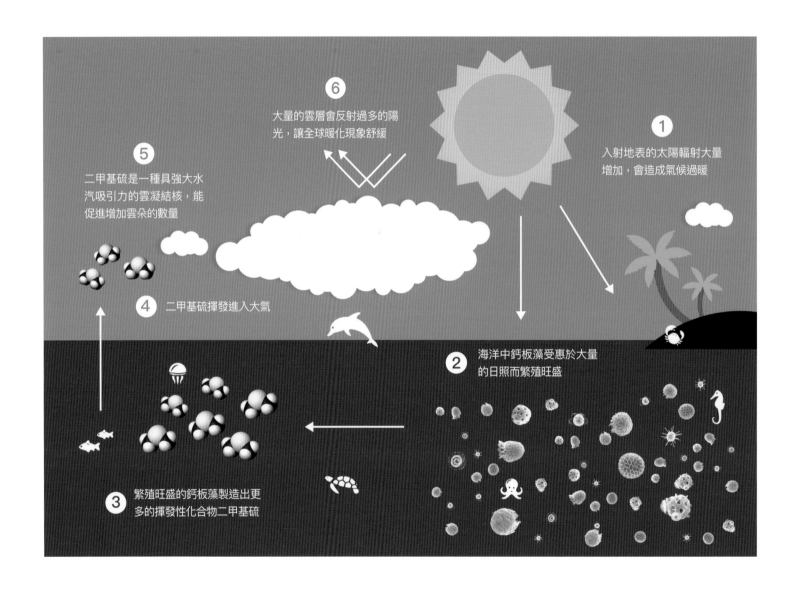

6 大量的雲層會反射過多的陽光，讓全球暖化現象舒緩

1 入射地表的太陽輻射大量增加，會造成氣候過暖

5 二甲基硫是一種具強大水汽吸引力的雲凝結核，能促進增加雲朵的數量

4 二甲基硫揮發進入大氣

2 海洋中鈣板藻受惠於大量的日照而繁殖旺盛

3 繁殖旺盛的鈣板藻製造出更多的揮發性化合物二甲基硫

蓋婭的空調器：穩定地球溫度

Gaia's Thermostat: Stabilizing the Atmosphere's Temperature

洛夫洛克於一九七零年代提出蓋婭假說，將生物圈與水圈、氣圈、地圈所構築的地球系統視為一個互相依賴、不可分離的整體。大地之母能夠自我調節，以達到共存共榮的看法。

以氣候系統為例，鈣板藻會因應地球溫度變化而調整其分泌二甲基硫的量，影響雲朵在大氣層中的遮蓋率，進而控制地表所接受到的日照量，以維持氣候系統不過熱，也不過冷。這種藉由生物與氣候系統互動，能達成動態卻又穩定的負回饋機制。

The Gaia Hypothesis was proposed by James Lovelock in the 1970s. It treats the biosphere, hydrosphere, atmosphere, and geosphere as an interdependent and inseparable system. The Mother Earth, called Gaia, as a whole can be self-regulating to sustain environmental optimum for contemporary life.

Taking climate system as an example, the coccolithophore may adjust the production of dimethyl sulfide in response to changes in the earth's temperature, so as to affect the coverage of the clouds in the atmosphere and to control the amount of solar radiation received by the earth's surface. In such a process, phytoplankton acts to minimize the temperature variations of the atmosphere. The tiny creature interacts with the climate system efficiently to maintain a dynamic stability of the earth's environment via a negative feedback loop.

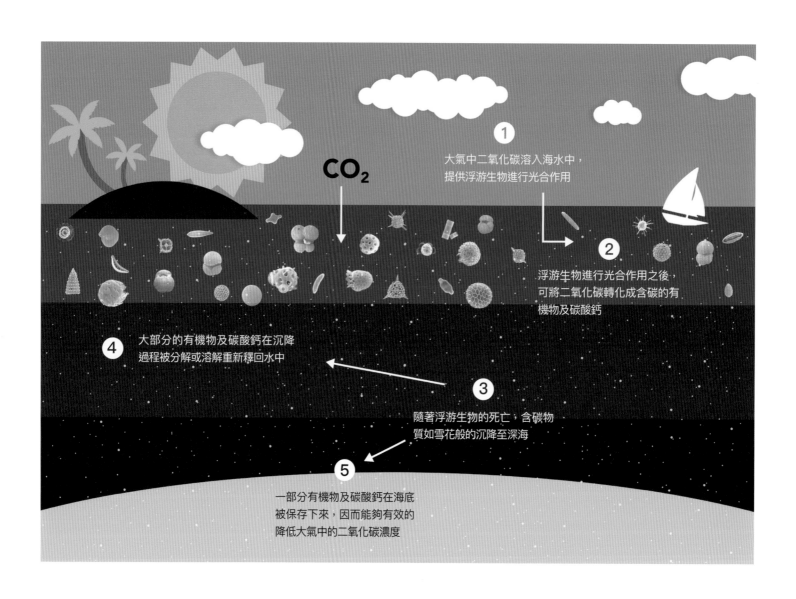

2

生物幫浦：調節二氧化碳的幫手
Biological Pump: Removing Carbon Dioxide by the Plankton

海洋浮游生物亦能藉由「生物幫浦」的運作移除大氣中二氧化碳，其原理在於二氧化碳能夠溶於海水，提供浮游生物行光合作用之用，當其死後如雪花般的沉降至深海，便能將含碳有機組成或碳酸鈣殼體自上層水體移除，此一過程得以有效調降大氣中的二氧化碳濃度。

在全球暖化危機逐漸逼近的今天，學者提出各類地球工法試圖解決此一危機。理論上，如果將生物幫浦的功率放大一點，可以降低二氧化碳濃度，例如透過施放鐵肥，科學家確實能短暫提升這個生物幫浦的功率。儘管如此，對於生態的可能衝擊仍有所未知。

The biological pump, driven by the marine plankton, transfers the carbon dioxide from the atmosphere to the deep sea water and sediment. The fact is that carbon dioxide can be dissolved in seawater to provide the plankton for photosynthesis and calcification. When planktons die, they sink to the deep sea like a snowflake and thus, the organic components and calcium carbonate shells are removed from the upper ocean. These processes can effectively lower carbon dioxide concentration in the atmosphere.

As the global warming is continuous deterioration, researchers have proposed various kinds of Earth engineering techniques to mitigate this issue. In theory, the biological pump could be enhanced efficiently under certain circumstances of human interference. By using iron fertilizer, scientists had verified a significantly increased carbon output to the deep sea. However, the potential of ecological impact is still unknown.

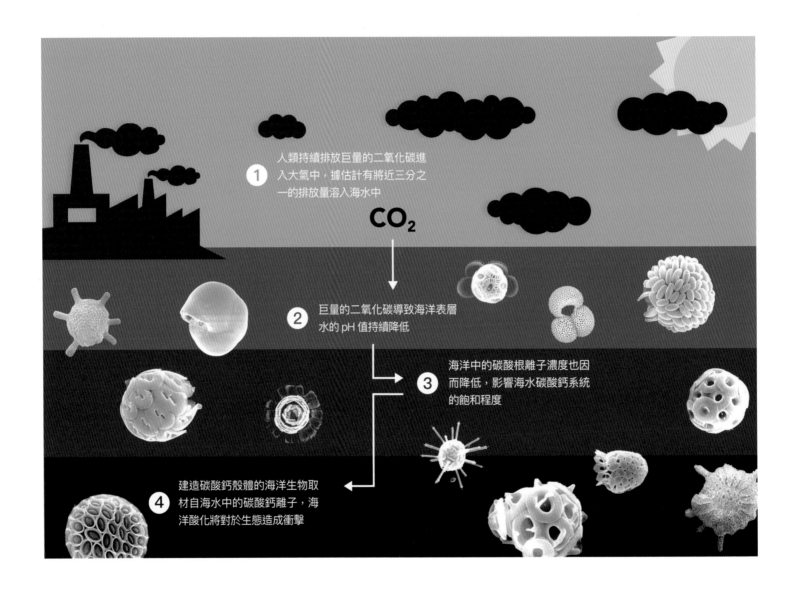

1 人類持續排放巨量的二氧化碳進入大氣中，據估計有將近三分之一的排放量溶入海水中

CO_2

2 巨量的二氧化碳導致海洋表層水的 pH 值持續降低

3 海洋中的碳酸根離子濃度也因而降低，影響海水碳酸鈣系統的飽和程度

4 建造碳酸鈣殼體的海洋生物取材自海水中的碳酸鈣離子，海洋酸化將對於生態造成衝擊

3

海洋酸化：海洋文明病
Ocean Acidification:
The Marine Civilization Disease

二氧化碳排導致全球暖化之外，科學家近年持續關注海洋酸化所衍生的潛在危機。工業革命以來，人類持續排放巨量的二氧化碳進入大氣，據估計有將近三分之一的排放量進入海洋，導致海洋表層水的 pH 值持續降低，碳酸根離子濃度也因而降低，影響海水碳酸鈣系統的飽和程度，稱之為海洋酸化。

許多海洋生物能夠建造碳酸鈣殼體或骨架，仰賴取材自水體中的碳酸鈣離子，一旦飽和狀況持續惡化，將對於海洋生態造成嚴重衝擊。儘管海洋目前所量測到的 pH 值仍呈弱鹼性，海洋生態學家仍發出警訊，企圖在尚未造成更大的海洋浩劫前能降低衝擊。

In addition to the issue of carbon dioxide emissions leading to global warming, scientists concerned about the potential impact caused by ocean acidification. Since the Industrial Revolution began, human activity has emitted huge amounts of carbon dioxide into the atmosphere. Nearly one-third of the emissions are estimated to enter the ocean reservoir, resulting in the ongoing decrease in the pH value and the carbonate ions in surface ocean. The decrease in the concentration of carbonate ions decreases the saturation state, and hence makes carbonate dissolution more likely.

Many marine organisms take up calcium and carbonate from the seawater to build shell and skeleton. The decrease in the amount of carbonate ions makes them more difficult to form biogenic carbonate, which is vulnerable to dissolution. The ongoing ocean acidification may still deteriorate continuously as to impact marine ecosystem. Although the pH value currently measured in the oceans is alkaline, marine ecologists issue warnings in an attempt to prevent their potential impact on marine ecology.

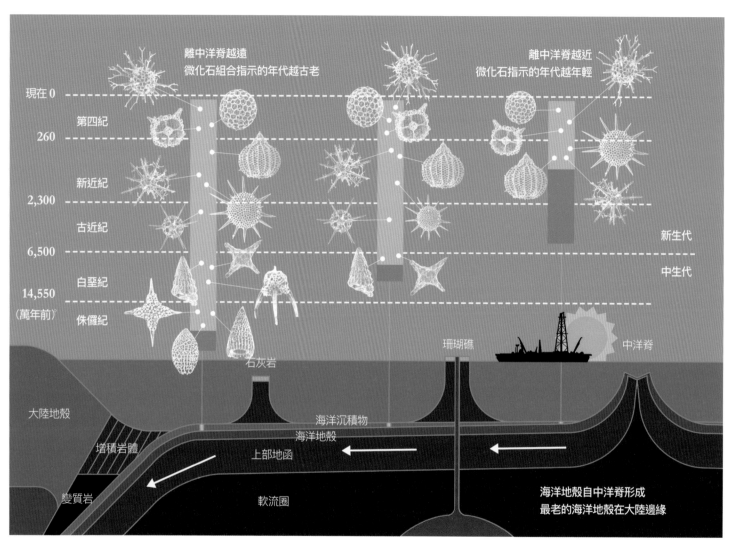

離中洋脊越遠
微化石組合指示的年代越古老

離中洋脊越近
微化石指示的年代越年輕

現在 0

第四紀

260

新近紀

2,300

古近紀

6,500

白堊紀

14,550

（萬年前）

侏儸紀

新生代

中生代

石灰岩

大陸地殼

增積岩體

變質岩

珊瑚礁

中洋脊

海洋沉積物

海洋地殼

上部地函

軟流圈

海洋地殼自中洋脊形成
最老的海洋地殼在大陸邊緣

圖上所用微化石僅供示意之用
並非代表實際生存年代

110

4

海洋岩芯鑽探：以古鑑今知未來
Drilling the Past: Exploring the Future

國際海洋鑽探計畫歷經三階段，長達半個世紀的演進，獲得豐碩的科學成果。一九六八年代執行計畫之初，運用挑戰者號為名的鑽井船從大西洋海床鑽取岩芯，發現從中洋脊向兩側的海洋地殼年齡越來越老，從而驗證了板塊構造學說。由於中洋脊持續張裂，大西洋兩岸仍將以每年二到三公分的速率背離著分開。

海床上累積的沉積物，各地厚度不一，年代也不同。根據沉積物最底層所保存的微化石，可以定出沉積物的年代，進而推導出覆蓋在沉積物之下的玄武岩形成年代。海洋地殼自中洋脊形成，沉積物厚度最薄，微化石組合指示的年代最年輕；最老的海洋地殼在大陸邊緣，沉積物年代約為一億八千萬年前。

For the past 50 years, the International Ocean Drilling Program has been going through three phases of progession to obtain massive achievements. The first drillship, Glomar Challenger, given its name as a tribute to the HMS Challenger, retrieved samples from the ocean floor since the 1968. These studies provided evidence to support the hypothesis of seafloor spreading and the theory of plate tectonic. As new oceanic crust is constantly being formed at the Mid-Atlantic Ridge, the coastlines on both sides of Atlantic still are leaving away at a speed of 2-3 cm/year.

The thickness of marine sediments depends largely on the length of its accumulation time. According to the microfossil collected from the base of sediments, micropaleontologist can datermine the age of the sediment and therefore the underlying ocean crust. As the youngest oceanic crust is formed at the mid-ocean ridge, the thickness of the sediment is relative thin. The oldest parts of the oceanic crust are distributed nearby continental margins with an age estimated of 180 million years old.

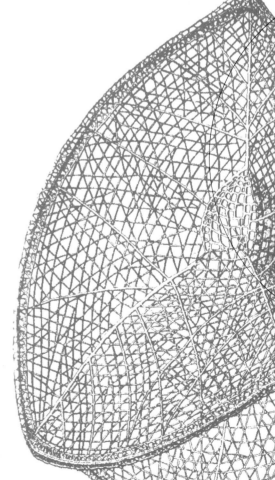

發行人　洪世佑

出版委員　洪世佑｜王逸群｜許毓純｜方建能｜吳嘉琦
　　　　　劉杏怡｜黃高駿｜方瓊德｜劉美珠

作者　李孟陽｜方建能

執行編輯　張羽嵐

助理編輯　蘇建華

美編設計　盧穎蓁

攝影　李孟陽｜葉貴玉｜王士偉｜楊天南｜汪良奇
　　　張詠斌｜莊智凱｜賴亞彤｜范綱祐｜張羽嵐

插圖　蔡力強

出版者　國立臺灣博物館
　　　　財團法人臺灣博物館文教基金會

地址　10046 臺北市襄陽路 2 號

電話　886-2-2382-2699

傳真　886-2-2382-2684

網址　http://www.ntm.gov.tw

出版日期　2018 年 12 月 初版二刷

印刷　新北市維凱創意印刷庇護工場

定價　570 元

ISBN　978-986-05-6195-1

微美幻境：海洋微化石 / 李孟陽，方建能著.
-- 初版二刷 . -- 臺北市：臺灣博物館，臺灣
博物館文教基金會 , 2018.12
　　面；　公分
ISBN 978-986-05-6195-1(平裝)

1. 微化石 2. 博物館特展
359.1　　　　　　　　　　107010055

本書由文化部及科技部核定之「古物新知—臺博館自然史藏品科技檢測計畫」補助